THE WORLD CALENDAR

THE WORLD CALENDAR

*Addresses and Occasional Papers
Chronologically Arranged on
the Progress of Calendar
Reform since 1930*

BY

ELISABETH ACHELIS

G. P. PUTNAM'S SONS
NEW YORK
1937

Our stability is but balance.
　　　　　　　　—Robert Bridges.

FOREWORD

In response to many requests, the material in this book has been assembled, consisting of various addresses and occasional papers by the President of The World Calendar Association.

Arranged chronologically, these papers serve to give a clear and logical account of the progress of the calendar reform movement since 1930. For all those interested in the remarkable advance which this movement has made during the past few years and the benefits which the reform will bring to civilization, the material is offered herewith in convenient and readily available form.

CONTENTS

THE WORLD CALENDAR

THE WORLD CALENDAR

All Years Alike
All Quarters Equal

First Quarter	Second Quarter	Third Quarter	Fourth Quarter

JANUARY

S	M	T	W	T	F	S
1	2	3	4	5	6	7
8	9	10	11	12	13	14
15	16	17	18	19	20	21
22	23	24	25	26	27	28
29	30	31				

APRIL

S	M	T	W	T	F	S
1	2	3	4	5	6	7
8	9	10	11	12	13	14
15	16	17	18	19	20	21
22	23	24	25	26	27	28
29	30	31				

JULY

S	M	T	W	T	F	S
1	2	3	4	5	6	7
8	9	10	11	12	13	14
15	16	17	18	19	20	21
22	23	24	25	26	27	28
29	30	31				

OCTOBER

S	M	T	W	T	F	S
1	2	3	4	5	6	7
8	9	10	11	12	13	14
15	16	17	18	19	20	21
22	23	24	25	26	27	28
29	30	31				

FEBRUARY

S	M	T	W	T	F	S
				1	2	3	4
5	6	7	8	9	10	11
12	13	14	15	16	17	18
19	20	21	22	23	24	25
26	27	28	29	30		

MAY

S	M	T	W	T	F	S
				1	2	3	4
5	6	7	8	9	10	11
12	13	14	15	16	17	18
19	20	21	22	23	24	25
26	27	28	29	30		

AUGUST

S	M	T	W	T	F	S
				1	2	3	4
5	6	7	8	9	10	11
12	13	14	15	16	17	18
19	20	21	22	23	24	25
26	27	28	29	30		

NOVEMBER

S	M	T	W	T	F	S
				1	2	3	4
5	6	7	8	9	10	11
12	13	14	15	16	17	18
19	20	21	22	23	24	25
26	27	28	29	30		

MARCH

S	M	T	W	T	F	S
					1	2
3	4	5	6	7	8	9
10	11	12	13	14	15	16
17	18	19	20	21	22	23
24	25	26	27	28	29	30

JUNE

S	M	T	W	T	F	S
					1	2
3	4	5	6	7	8	9
10	11	12	13	14	15	16
17	18	19	20	21	22	23
24	25	26	27	28	29	30
						**

SEPTEMBER

S	M	T	W	T	F	S
					1	2
3	4	5	6	7	8	9
10	11	12	13	14	15	16
17	18	19	20	21	22	23
24	25	26	27	28	29	30

DECEMBER

S	M	T	W	T	F	S
					1	2
3	4	5	6	7	8	9
10	11	12	13	14	15	16
17	18	19	20	21	22	23
24	25	26	27	28	29	30
						*

*YEAR-END DAY, December Y, follows December 30th every year
**LEAP-YEAR DAY, June L, follows June 30th in leap years

The World Calendar is a revision of the present calendar to correct its inequalities and discrepancies. It rearranges the length of the 12 months so that they are regular, making the year divisible into equal halves and quarters in a *"perpetual"* calendar. Every year is the same; every quarter identical.

In this new calendar, each quarter contains exactly three months, 13 weeks, 91 days. Each quarter begins on Sunday and ends on Saturday. The first month in each quarter has 31 days, and the other two 30 days each. Every month has 26 weekdays.

In order to make the calendar perpetual (identical for every year), at the same time retaining astronomical accuracy, the 365th day of the year, called Year-End Day, is an intercalary day placed between December 30th and January 1st and considered an extra Saturday. The 366th day in leap years, called Leap-Year Day, is intercalated between June 30th and July 1st on another extra Saturday. These intercalary or stabilizing days are tabulated as December Y, or 31, and June L, or 31, and would probably be observed as international holidays. January 1st, New Year's Day, always falls on Sunday.

The revised calendar is balanced in structure, perpetual in form, harmonious in arrangement. It conforms to the solar year of 365.2422 days and to the natural seasons. Besides its advantages in economy and efficiency, it facilitates statistical comparisons, coordinates the different time-periods, and stabilizes religious and secular holidays. As compared with any other proposal for calendar revision, it offers an adjustment in which the transition from the old to the new order can be made without disturbance.

1

AMERICAN BAR ASSOCIATION

Address, March 24, 1931

IN ALL world-wide movements of vast significance we always find in the vanguard the esteemed profession of the law; the law that protects rights, prevents injustice, and avoids, whenever possible, increase of litigation. In my childhood I was taught to respect in greater measure the lawyer who discouraged his clients from going to court rather than the lawyer who invited court action, and this viewpoint and belief in the higher aspect of the law has a direct bearing on the subject in hand, the simplification of the calendar.

Calendar revision will have its preliminary discussion before the Committee of Communications and Transit of the League of Nations at Geneva in May or June, and subsequently at the international conference of the League in October. To this meeting all member states and non-member nations of the League have been invited. You will see, therefore, how timely is our interest in this movement for calendar reform, and the urgency of giving it careful study and decisive action.

I believe we all agree that the present Gregorian Calendar is unsatisfactory and are willing to devote discussion to an improvement. But up to the present time, prominent associations like your own have withheld taking any action on a definite choice of plan. Such an action on your part now would be a stimulus very much needed, and because of it, I am glad to bring the plan of The World Calendar to you. You know as I do that in all important subjects several plans under discussion are always better than the presentation of just one.

We understand that on previous occasions, your Committee listened to a representative of Mr. George Eastman, chairman of the National Committee on Calendar Simplification, who spoke for the International Fixed Calendar, a plan which advocates a 13-month year. This project stresses the four-week month and emphasizes the week as the important unit upon which to base a new system. Since you know this plan, we shall not enter into its description nor discuss its merits or demerits. We shall talk chiefly of The World Calendar.

This plan retains the present 12-month year which is divided equally into half-years and quarter-years. Such an arrangement eliminates the many irregularities which annoy civilization at the present time. By establishing an equal-quarter year one secures the needed equation for comparability which is essential for scientific data, business reports and statistical records. An orderly system of days with their dates is also helpful for social, civic, national and international relationships.

Now, as to its description:—The quarters are divided into three months or 13 weeks or 91 days. The first month in each quarter has 31 days and begins on the *first* day of the week, Sunday; the second or *middle* month has 30 days and begins on the *middle* day of the week, Wednesday; and the third and *last* month of 30 days begins on the *last* day of the full working-week, Friday. Each month then has 26 week-days. Every quarter is alike, but the three months within these quarters vary slightly; thus the months escape the stultifying effect of a continued sameness and the calendar is not confined to a rigid monotony.

The changes involve only seven days. Two days, the 29th and 30th of February, are added; the 31st day of March is taken away; while to April is given a 31st day. The 31st of May and August are eliminated, and the seventh date, the 31st of December, is converted to Year-End Day. From February 28th to September 1st the transfer of dates between the old and new calendars does not affect these months more than two dates, while between September 1st and the following February 28th, almost six months, the dates remain unaltered. Such an adjustment is simple for historical and legal records, text books, encyclopaedias, etc.

The left-over 365th day at the end of the year has ever been the perplexing problem in calendar reform. Nature in her indefinable wisdom has devised our year to be slightly irregular in its number of days in so far as the true solar year, upon which our calendar is based, is not divisible into round numbers. So it appears that nature is subtly preventing man from becoming too set and rigid in his method of counting time. The advocates of The World Calendar are keenly aware of nature's variableness and they endeavor to work in harmony with this distinctive characteristic. The odd day, therefore, which is our present December 31st, will be called Year-End Day and be placed between Saturday, December 30th, and Sunday, January 1st. Its week-day name will be a second or extra Saturday, and its suggested tabulation is December Y. (Y denotes the first letter of Year-End Day, thereby designating at a glance the distinctive feature.) The idea of placing the 365th day on a second Saturday is scientifically and legally sound. We all know and accept the extra day which every traveller gains when he journeys from the Eastern to the Western Hemisphere and crosses the international date line at the 180th Meridian in the Pacific. Rear-Admiral Richard E. Byrd tells us how his Antarctic expedition spent two Christmases under similar conditions, and how he declared the second Christmas day the official one.

The World Calendar recognizes the *year* as the basic unit of time-measurement. The year always begins on the first day of the week, Sunday, which preserves the sacred significance of that day with its following seventh-day Saturday coming in regular order. It always ends the year on Year-End Day which does not break into the week, as it comes at the close of the week and completes the year, thus conserving inviolate the last seventh day of the week, namely Saturday. With this extra Saturday, Year-End Day, following December 30th, would become an international holiday upon which all nations could join in hopeful anticipation of a new year while bidding farewell to the old.

Leap Day, the extra quadrennial day, is placed on a new day in midsummer between the end of June and the beginning of July. It has its name, its day and date, like Year-End Day; in this instance Leap-Year Day, also a second Saturday, following June 30th is dated June L on the same principle as Year-End Day. Is it not strange that reformers in the other suggested plans have generally neglected to give Year-End Day and Leap-Year Day a place in the week? Especially in law such a situation would seem quite untenable.

But now let us consider how skilfully The World Calendar avoids difficulties by retaining the 12-month year. In considering the 13-month proposal, it is obvious that when the division of time is increased there must follow an increase in every other direction, which will be burdensome as it affects daily activities. Life and Time are so closely inter-related that any change along these lines would seriously affect mankind in many ways. By the rearrangement of the year into equal half- and quarter-divisions, without disturbing its fundamental structure of 12 months, and without adding an extra (13th) month, annoying fractions are avoided, calculations are simplified, and the work of accountants and the mailing of monthly statements are not increased. The World Calendar, in contrast to the 13th month plan, saves material in the use of stamps and stationery. It does not add to energy, labor, time and expense, as for example, in the editing of monthly publications, or in the preparation of the quarterly and semi-annual statistical reports which are necessary in all kinds of business and scientific fields. It does not impose on the home an extra 13th visit from rent collectors, or an additional expense in the reading of meters for water, gas and electricity, a business expense which the consumer must share. It does not necessitate the mailing and paying of an extra 13th bill, and it does not complicate many other details which are connected with family life and the budget.

In government and financial fields, loans, bonds, mortgages, long term leases and contracts call for little readjustment if any,—at the most a slight change in writing to avoid possible litigation.

It has been frequently stated that a four-week month arrangement would simplify the weekly pay roll, and that "split-week" payments would thus be eliminated. This is true when one looks only at the week as the chief unit of the year. When one considers, however, that three months, 13 weeks or 91 days exist in every quarter of the year, one can readily see that the three-month quarter-year is easier for calculation and comparability than a 3¼ month division of the 13-month scheme. Concentrating upon the week narrows and limits one's vision, whereas the broader outlook of the quarter- and half-year division enlarges and clarifies one's viewpoint and gives a better perspective in business, in daily living and world events.

It is problematical also whether an added monthly salary would be an advantage, when you consider that the expenses of another month in the year might offset all the gain.

The writer of a recent magazine article claims that our modern industrial age needs an industrialized calendar, that therefore we ought to drop the present one because it was developed in an agricultural age. This is an error. The onus of our unsatisfactory calendar rests not so much upon agriculture as upon the vain arrogance of a Roman Emperor of 2,000 years ago. A workable calendar for all time transcends any special age, just as limitless Time resists being rigidly catalogued. Agriculture, industry, science, economics, administration, religion, and civil and social activities dovetail so nicely that a line of demarcation is not advisable nor often even possible. Harmony of intercourse assures a wholesome balance upon which the stability of civilization rests. The attempt, therefore, to identify the calendar with any one field of activity is unjust, and the law should be ever watchful to prevent such an effort toward appropriation. The World Calendar in its regulated arrangement recognizes these existing conditions and works in harmony with all of them.

Progressive students of the calendar agree that placing holidays on a Monday, whenever possible, would be of great benefit to mankind, and the advocates of The World Calendar heartily uphold this principle. It is a happy coincidence that in the plan which The World Calendar Association is endorsing, Christmas automatically falls on Monday, December 25. It calls for no change. Easter would be observed on April 8, which follows closely the historical date, rather than on April 15, since to many people the latter date is closely associated with matters inappropriate to the commemoration of the Resurrection. We advocate continuing to celebrate the Fourth of July on that date because of its historical significance, notwithstanding that it falls on a Wednesday in the revised calendar.

The World Calendar is quite up to date in combining two national holidays in one week-end by celebrating Washington's birthday on Saturday, February 11, and Lincoln's birthday on Monday, February 13. It is historically correct that the father of our country was born on February 11, the date which Washington himself always considered his birthday, and it was only due to the change from the Julian to the Gregorian calendar in 1752 that the original date was changed by the new style, to February 22nd. By thus establishing a three-day weekend period we can honor the birthdays of Washington and Lincoln together, which is a simplification much to be desired.

From thoughts like these it appears to me, a woman of a home, that The World Calendar means economy in daily living and a saving in domestic and business energy, labor and time. The plan offers not only an economic gain but, of far greater importance to human welfare, an ordered freedom within a flexible regularity. Our daily life is simplified under this calendar; time and energy are conserved; holidays are stabilized; the year is regulated and balanced; and the transition from the old to the new is made easy by retention of the 12-month year, revised and reformed to meet modern requirements.

Again may I ask you to study carefully the movement for calendar reform and register your preferences as to a choice of plan. In closing, let me remind you of the two major plans under discussion in the United States—the 13-month International Fixed Calendar and The World Calendar, which calls for an improved 12-month year. The prestige of the American Bar Association has its responsibilities—it is widely relied upon to point the way to ordinary citizens whose customary thought is not judicial. You can do no better service at this time than to lend your talents and experience to an approval of a definite calendar plan. The League Conference at Geneva can hardly fail to consider the serious endorsement of such a professional body as this one.

II

APPEAL TO WOMEN

Address before the Wednesday Afternoon Club,
New York City, April 15, 1931

TO many women, the subject of calendar reform is so new and strange that we wonder why we should bother about it now, when there are so many pressing and serious questions to be solved. However, you will realize the importance of knowing about calendar reform when I tell you that it is here, close at our doors. Unless we awake to the imminence of a change in the calendar we may find ourselves faced with some form of revision which we may not like or approve. Because of this possibility we ought to find out where we stand and make our opinions nationally heard. World governments are meeting to study this question at Geneva on June 8 of this year and again, still more officially, five months later in October, when it is hoped some definite decision may be reached.

If we go back to history, we find that changes in the calendar have been made at frequent intervals. The ancients measured time by the moon because the moon's regular phases were easier to study than the movements of the stars and the sun. The Egyptian astronomers were among the first scientists to study more accurately the sun's influence upon our globe. They not only discovered the seasonal year, but they put it into practical use. Their year had three separate periods of four months each. These three periods were as follows: The inundation or fertilizing season; the winter or sowing season; and the summer or harvesting season. With this knowledge they were able to produce more frequent and better crops by basing their calendar on the sun's influence rather than on the phases of the moon.

When the illustrious Roman, Julius Caesar, conquered Egypt, he unearthed the secret of the Egyptian calendar system and then made it the basis of his famous calendar reform. He adopted the 12-month arrangement; to the uneven months he allotted 31 days; to the even months he allotted 30 days with the exception of February, which was defrauded and given only 29 days in common years in order to keep the year to its 365 days and 6 hours. Leap year was inaugurated every four years, which took care of those extra 6 hours by waiting until they accumulated to one complete day. This added day was given to impoverished February, so that at least in leap years, it had the same number of days as the other even months. Unfortunately, Caesar was assassinated soon after he initiated his reform, and the application of the calendar was left to his vain successor, Augustus. Now this nephew was filled with a consuming desire to equal in importance his distinguished uncle and as Julius had a month named July, Augustus decided to name the following month "August" after himself. After this was done, Augustus noticed that his month had only 30 days, which did not suit him at all. To correct this, he tampered still further with the calendar by adding an extra day to his month, August, and taking it away from the already shortened February. Then, to avoid three successive 31-day months, he rearranged the last four months of the year by giving 31 days to the last two even months and 30 days to the last two odd ones. And thus we acquired our present irregular calendar!

The Julian system considered the year, as we have said, to be 365 days and 6 hours long. Actually it is slightly shorter. After many centuries this miscalculation, together with the early observance of too many leap years, brought the Julian year 10 days out of gear with actual astronomical reckonings. Pope Gregory XIII corrected this gap of days by his famous reform in 1582 A.D. when 10 days were skipped by some nations and 11 days by others, according to the time when the different nations adopted it. It was unfortunate that this Gregorian reform did not completely correct the irregularities of the calendar, and it is amazing that the modern world has been willing so long to abide by them.

The main defects in our present calendar lie in its disproportionate arrangement. How many of us here present know on what day April 15 will fall next year, the year following, or in five years hence? To regulate the year into some systematic order by which we can tell such things, would be of great advantage. It can be arranged simply and easily without upsetting our present system too much.

Another fault in our calendar is the unsystematic inequality of the months and the quarters of the year. For purposes of records, statistical comparisons and business reports, these irregularities are great obstacles. The first quarter of the year, as we now have it, has 90 days, the second 91, while the third and fourth have 92 days each. There is no reason why the four quarters, representing the four seasons, should not have a perfect equality, by which easy comparability would be secured.

The months, too, vary considerably. If May of last

year had five Saturdays and five Sundays, it is certain
that it will not have the same number this year. As we
have said, we never know from year to year on what
week-day a certain date will fall; the months differ in
length arbitrarily; the quarter and half-years are not
evenly apportioned; Saturdays and Sundays vary in number between four or five to a month, and holidays come
on week-days or Sundays, with Christmas and Easter
always shifting either as to day or date.

But patience has its limitations and the world seems to
have been annoyed long enough. For the past hundred
years, students and scientists have frequently come forward with suggestions for improvement. The League of
Nations, in 1923, formed its first committee to study this
question and nearly 200 different plans are now on file.
Many of them are too radical and fantastic for practical
minds to accept.

Therefore it should be the purpose of calendar reformers to study the problem from the angles of astronomy and commerce, and from educational, social and
religious standpoints. This is precisely what The World
Calendar Association has done.

First of all, The World Calendar retains the fundamental structure of the 12 months. The calendar for
each quarter is identical and the arrangement of months
within each quarter is the same although the lengths of
the three months differ slightly, retaining a *pleasing
variety* without disturbing the ordered equality of the
quarters. By keeping to the 12-month arrangement, the
practical custom of monthly payments is not altered, reduced or increased.

The calendar is made "perpetual" so that every year's
calendar is identical, by the device known as "intercal-

ation." You are familiar from your study of The World Calendar Plan, with the principle of the "Year-End Day" and the "Leap-Year Day." We frankly admit our amazement at the many strange and fantastic ways in which calendar reformers have endeavored to side-track these two days by calling them "blank days." We also wonder how such reformers expect to place and to record a "blank day" in their yearly budget and records, when the day has no weekday place. Other reformers submit plans whereby these two days are allowed to accumulate until they aggregate an extra 53rd week every five or six years, or an extra 13-month year every 20 years or so, in an attempt to catch up with astronomical conditions. What a strange calendar it would be, wherein the year would always be either too short or too long, and where occasional "extraordinary" or "exceptional" years would be our fate! It does seem that revision of the calendar should make our year a practical one, and that it should be astronomically correct at the same time.

An advocate of the 13-month year recently wrote in a popular magazine: "Commerce and industry cannot wait for the leisurely succession of the seasons. Their decisions must be made more frequently. They are, therefore, obliged to use the shorter periods of months and weeks." We look with apprehension on any proposed calendar that so carelessly disregards the astronomical seasons. The seasonal year is a vital factor in our lives, whether we live in the temperate zone, the tropical belt or near the frigid areas of the two poles. Rear-Admiral Byrd could not, if he tried, ignore the darkened winter season in his Antarctic expeditions. And what would happen to agriculture, horticulture and all other seasonable businesses if the seasons were ignored in calendar reckonings? Does not much of the fun which women have in getting new winter and summer clothes, hats and shoes depend on the seasonal correctness of the calendar? Do not the winter and summer divisions of the calendar have a direct bearing on our travelers?

Weekly accountings in business are perhaps necessary in some lines, but as the artist who paints in detail his canvas, steps back every once in a while to get a better perspective of the whole picture, so our commercial and business men have to step back and take a wider view of their affairs through the quarterly and semi-annual reports by which they gauge the trend of commerce and industry. I know of no business which can afford to concentrate too minutely on the week, at the sacrifice of the larger division of quarters with their completely rounded out three months.

The question of holidays, too, is important in any plan for calendar revision. The World Calendar advocates the placing of holidays on Mondays whenever possible. Easter, whose wandering tendency has been the despair of educators, stylists and travelers for generations, should be established on a definite Sunday in April, preferably April 8, which comes nearest the historical day of its occurrence. Because of financial obligations often associated with the fifteenth of a month, April 15, the date favored in some of the other plans, is less acceptable. A materialistic note might creep in on this religious holiday which would be alien to the spirit of the Resurrection. Of course, the decision of the Easter date is primarily a religious affair and rests with the various church authorities.

Labor Day, which marks the end of the summer season, and the beginning of the school year, will come on a regular date, instead of slipping as it does in the present calendar through a period of seven days during the first week of September. In The World Calendar, it would be September 4 or it might be postponed to a week later, if more desirable, to September 11.

Christmas, December 25, naturally falls on a Monday, affording us an extended weekend. All our cherished associations will be preserved, and no distressful readjustment of the Christmas date will be necessary in the proposed calendar revision.

The changes involved in this plan of reform amount to only seven days in number—two days added to the end of February, one added to the end of April and the last day taken from March, May and August. The 31st day of December will be called Year-End Day and will be regarded as an extra Saturday or December Y—in order to make the new year always begin on Sunday. Dates during the six months from February 28 to September 1 will undergo a change of one or two days, while those in the other six months, September 1 to February 28, will remain as they are.

One of the great advantages of The World Calendar plan lies in the fact that the transition to it is easy, pleasant and free from confusion. Once it is adopted our calendar will be perpetual. No rhymes will have to be memorized to remind us of the length of the months, because we shall know automatically when any certain date will fall. April 15 will always be on a Sunday, while May 15 will always come on a Wednesday, and June 15 on a Friday. School activities, household planning and holiday arrangements will become simplified and thus be more enjoyable. The World Calendar is practical and ideal.

The other major plan of calendar reform has a forceful and insistent body of supporters. To our minds nothing could be more dangerous than that their 13-month scheme should receive approval of the League of Nations or of European governments or the sanction of our own national government. You will remember that at the beginning of this article I suggested that some plan might be forced upon us which we would not like or approve, a plan alien to all that is best for our general welfare.

The advocates of the 13-month plan propose that our calendar contain 13 rigidly identical months of four weeks each, with a new 13th month to be called Sol inserted between June and July. To me, the mechanical precision of these months would certainly be most irksome. Routine and rigidity of this kind is hardly consistent with feminine nature, which finds it difficult to endure any restricting monotony. I have heard many women declare that to accept this radical and revolutionary proposal would throw the world into chaos. My imagination utterly fails me when I try to conceive what such a tampering might mean.

The scheme has attracted a following, mainly, I think, because it is novel, methodical and mechanically neat. There are many people who pride themselves on following every new thing, no matter how extreme it may be.

Opposition to the 13-month plan should not be merely negative. It should be constructive. It should support a more practical and reasonable revision, one which retains the good features of the present calendar and at the same time remedies its defects.

A friend recently described a calendar thus: "A calendar is to time what a map is to space. Calendar divisions serve to designate days; map divisions serve to designate locations. The primary unit of calendar division is a date;

the primary unit of map division is—an address. But when you try to designate dates as you would designate street-addresses, you find a situation—as at present—as if streets shifted from city to city; as if cities wandered back and forth across the borders of states; as if states shrank back and forth within the varying borders of a country."

In our study of calendar reform let us keep in mind that the minor activities of life are associated with the day, the major activities with the seasons and the whole cycle of activities with the completed year. All these time-periods are of astronomical origin and should be used to work in harmony with each other.

It is true that the civilized world is committed, for social and religious conveniences, to the week and month. The 13-month calendar reconciles the weeks with the month but abandons the quarterly seasons. This unnecessary and faulty departure from the seasonal quarter and from the customary accepted 12-month division of the year are experiments too risky to take. The confusion and litigation that would result are impossible to foresee. Why abandon our present 12-month system, tried for ages and found satisfactory, when all that is needed is a slight simplification and modification to correct the present defects?

A banker, commenting on the 13-month proposal said to me: "I shudder to think how it would complicate interest calculations." To reckon monthly payment by a thirteenth of a year certainly is not practical with the difficult number 13 to deal with when the revised and practical 12-month year of The World Calendar has every advantage, wherein the customary 12-month payments, accounts and general transactions are not altered, reduced or increased. Then, too, there is the added simplification of equalized quarter-years which are necessary for accurate comparisons.

Women's clubs and study groups everywhere can give helpful cooperation in bringing to their friends, acquaintances and the public a consideration of this important subject of calendar revision. Individual efforts, interest and enthusiasm are much needed to arouse public opinion. We can and will succeed only if we all do our best, be it little or great, toward attaining this desirable end.

III

LEAGUE OF NATIONS

Address at Geneva, June 9, 1931

IT is a great privilege to attend these meetings and
to find such keen interest everywhere in the subject
of calendar reform.

All of us who are working in this cause have begun
to feel, I think, that simplification of the calendar is a
duty which we owe to posterity. We are not planning this
change because of the benefits that it will bring to us or
to our contemporaries, but rather for future generations
and in fact for all time to come. The old calendar is
inconsistent with the new age which is being born into
this old world. The old calendar is ill adapted to the
needs of the next generation, which must live and move
and have its being in the midst of surroundings even
more practical, more exact and more scientifically precise
than those in which we have lived.

There is no dispute as to the defects of the present
calendar. There is no real difference of opinion as to the
need of rectifying them. Some observers think that the
time is not yet ripe, and there are various convictions
as to the best method of rectification. But we are all
agreed as to the fundamental desirability of change.

I have the honor to represent The World Calendar Association of the United States, which has been making

a sincere study of the calendar situation since its organization last autumn.

Our attention was drawn to this subject by the earnest
and painstaking work of Mr. Eastman and his associates.
Their energy and enthusiasm have been an example and an
inspiration to all reformers.   Mr. Eastman's leadership
has aroused universal interest, calling attention to the
defects of the calendar and to the impelling need for improvement.   The persistence and zeal of Dr. Marvin, Mr.
Cotsworth, Colonel Solbert, Mr. Stiles and others are also
appreciated and gratefully acknowledged.   Without their
consistent and loyal efforts for improvement in the calendar this movement would not have advanced so far.

From the beginning of our study on this question, however, we became convinced that the 13-month plan,
which these gentlemen have so ably advocated, was too
extreme and unnecessarily disturbing for general acceptance in America.   The World Calendar Association was
organized to advance a more moderate plan, an improved
12-month year of equal-quarter divisions which would
have a better chance of adoption among all peoples; the
conservatives as well as the progressives.

Since the incorporation of this association we have approached about 100,000 Americans in various fields of
activity—transportation, journalism, agriculture, commerce, finance, religion, education and science.   Within
the past three months more than 2500 persons have joined
our membership, whose steady growth is an indication of
an encouraging and wide-spread interest in the calendar.

Among our more recent activities to determine how far
the 12-month calendar was favored in the United States,
we issued a questionnaire to the entire membership of a
typical American Chamber of Commerce, that located in

Wilmington, Delaware, which has 1200 members. With the full cooperation of the officers of this Chamber, we invited their opinion on calendar reform. We took the greatest care that each member was precisely informed.* The proposed 13-month revision was placed before them as presented by its advocates, and on a parallel page was shown the arrangement of an improved 12-month year, The World Calendar.

The result, we believe, gives a fair test of the present opinion of American business. It shows the following percentages:

Business men opposed to calendar reform 32.3%
Business men favoring 13-month calendar 30.3%
Business men favoring 12-month calendar 37.4%

You will note the significance of these percentages. A clear majority, nearly 68%, expressed themselves in favor of calendar reform. The minority who opposed all calendar change are perhaps mostly people who are not yet fully informed of the situation and its need. The eventual proportion of these who will continue to oppose all calendar reform will be very small, we believe.

As to the majority who favor calendar reform, it is interesting to note that considerably more than half of those who replied gave their approval to the 12-month revision. There is no reason to suppose that this statistical proportion in favor of the 12-month plan will not be

* The text of the questionnaire submitted to members of the Wilmington Chamber of Commerce was as follows: "Are you in favor of calendar reform? (Answer yes or no) .... If so, do you favor the 13-month calendar plan or the retention of a 12-month calendar, improved? (Answer with numerals 12 or 13) .... Would the correction of calendar irregularities, in your opinion, be a help or an economy to business? (Answer yes or no) .... Remarks .... (Name) ...."

found approximately correct for any similar cross section of American business opinion.

. I may say in passing that this result differs considerably from that of the questionnaires reported by the Eastman Committee. But this difference is mainly due to the fact that the 12-month plan presented by the Eastman Committee in its questionnaires was a particularly bad example of a 12-month revision and probably not clearly understood by most of those who answered.

American advocates of the 13-month plan lay great stress on the fact that 140 business concerns are using a 13-month system of 28 days for their own business accounting. When one considers the active propaganda that has been so ably carried on by the Eastman Committee for several years in an effort to secure the adoption of a 13-month calendar, it is amazing that the result is not greater. We are told that the total of 140 American firms is less than $\frac{1}{50}$th of 1% of all business concerns in America. This is so small a proportion that it indicates a majority of business firms are at least indifferent to the 13-month arrangement.

In our correspondence with various European groups we have found the same intelligent interest in the whole subject of calendar reform as in America. It has seemed to us that European opinion was concentrating around the 12-month plan. The Swiss Committee, for example, has stood squarely in favor of a plan of this kind, and a similar attitude was evidenced to us by important groups in Germany, Italy and Belgium.

Great Britain has not shown any indifference, but conservative British opinion has voiced an opposition to the 13-month plan that has seemed considerably stronger than any corresponding advocacy of the 12-month alternative.

France, according to our correspondents, cannot hope to get any real popular support for so radical a change as the 13-month plan, but may consent to a 12-month revision, which our correspondents believe would pass almost unnoticed.

From our studies both in the United States and in Europe, we have been led to the conclusion that it would be better for all national groups and committees to concentrate their efforts on the 12-month plan, on the ground that this plan would everywhere be more acceptable and would stand a better chance of success.

As a representative of The World Calendar Association, I regret exceedingly that the Swiss Committee is unable to be present at these hearings, for I am sure they would have presented their 12-month plan ably and well. The great value of their plan, as reported December, 1930, and that of The World Calendar, both of which are alike in their equal quarter-year arrangement, lies in their simplicity and efficiency. I shall outline briefly the outstanding advantages gained by the acceptance of this type of an equal-quarter-year proposal:

> The revised 12-month year becomes the equal multiple of halves and quarters, thirds and sixths; it is regular in arrangement and stabilized; the even quarters conform as they do now to the seasons, recognizing natural laws; every month has the same number of 26 week days; comparisons are easily obtained; changes involved require a minimum of adjustment; expenses are not increased for business and the consumer; religious and secular holidays are stabilized; and the transition from the old to the new order is made easy by the retention of the 12-month year.

Only seven days are changed; and dates, anniversaries and records of various descriptions call for no alterations in the dates between September 1 and February 28, while in the other six months the readjustments are so slight that they would be practically unnoticed by people everywhere.

The equal-quarter periods of the year consist of 91 days, 13 weeks or three months, of which the first month in each quarter has 31 days and the remaining two, 30 days each. The unequal quarter-divisions of the present Gregorian calendar, which vary between 90 and 92 days, are thereby corrected. This improvement, we believe, will meet with world-wide approval. The inauguration of the odd 365th Year-End Day and the extra 366th Leap-Year Day insures a yearly regularity and makes possible a perpetual calendar.

The World Calendar considers the year as the central point of the calendar. The year-cycle ends its annual round with Year-End Day, the old December 31, and begins its new one on Sunday, January 1, about the same time that the earth commences her next revolution around the sun. This brilliant orb in the heavens, and not man, is the direct cause of the vagaries of the odd day and the extra day within the annual and leap year circuits of the yearly cycles. The week and month are sub-divisions of the year. Every common year has its definite 52 weeks plus one day, and by retaining its 12-month structure, a four-quarter year is easily related to the four seasons. With this method in use, the year, the 12 months and the seven-day weeks, begin their annual round simultaneously.

The two intercalary days, Year-End Day and Leap-Year Day, are given a position in the week, placed on extra Saturdays and tabulated as December Y and June L. This of course is provisional. If the Committee prefers a more specific terminology, the odd 365th day might be called

"Sylvester" and dated December S, while the 366th day every leap year might be named "Bissextile" and dated June B. These days might well be considered as international holidays. By inserting these days between weeks, the seventh day in the week and the sequence of days within every week are upheld. The year always begins on the first day of the week, Sunday, January 1, and the last half of the year in leap years always commences on Sunday, July 1. It is obvious, I think, that when a day has its place in the week and month and is given a name, it cannot be a "blank day" or "dies non." The introduction of a double day in the reformed calendar is scientifically sound. It can be likened to that extra day which travellers add to their account when they cross the International Date Line on the Pacific.

We have noticed with interest and pleasure that the stabilizing of Easter is one of the main objectives of calendar reform. In America we have found both religious and secular opinion favorable to giving Easter a regular date. Sunday, April 8, which comes nearest to the historical date, seems the logical choice, but should this date prove too unseasonable for countries located in northern latitudes then Sunday, April 22, might be selected. As the 15th of a month is frequently associated with mid-monthly financial settlements, Sunday, April 15, does not appear to The World Calendar Association to be as acceptable.

In our studies into religious opinion in the United States we have found that liberal religious groups welcome a reasonable and logical method of calendar reform. There exists however, in the United States as in Europe, a considerable number of people who are disturbed by the use of the so-called intercalary days, Year-End Day and Leap-Year Day, which they regard as creating an eight-day week every year, thereby breaking into the succession of weeks.

Personally I have deep sympathy with the religious convictions of these objectors, although I cannot subscribe to their tenets. I wish they could be brought to realize that in the fourth period of creation the sun, the moon and the stars and the division of the seasons, the years and the days took place, while in the seventh period a day of rest was established. Few religious leaders have claimed with authority that successive weeks are of greater importance than a correct astronomical year. With an equal regard for both these periods of creation rather than an over-emphasis of the seven-day period, a possible solution of the present problem may be found.

All progressive reforms call for conciliations, and adjustments are inevitable when old theories are replaced by new interpretations gained by an increase in knowledge.

Religion is perhaps more closely affected by calendar reform than any other living force, but it has always been able to find a way to meet the changes which progress demanded. Religions, like peoples and nations, have often sacrificed cherished tradition at the call of a world-wide need.

Within the last century religion has had other problems to solve in connection with time-measurement. There were conscientious religious objectors to daylight saving time, and about 50 years ago in the United States, similar critics crusaded intensely against the adoption of standard time. In both these instances the storm was weathered and the objections eventually forgotten, without doing serious harm to religious sentiment.

IV

INTERNATIONAL VIEWPOINT

Report, in collaboration with C. D. Morris, to members of The World Calendar Association on the June 1931 meeting of the League of Nations.

WE found at Geneva a sincere and serious interest in the subject of calendar reform, and an obvious desire on the part of the League of Nations to give a sympathetic hearing to every phase of opinion, both pro and con. The League made its first recommendation in favor of a new calendar in 1923, and since that time it has gone forward, deliberately and painstakingly, in the study and advocacy of this reform. Wisely the League has shown no wish to move with undue haste in a matter which so vitally affects the daily life of every nation and people. Even today, after eight years, it feels keenly the necessity of building up in most countries a more lively understanding of the problem, before it makes a binding commitment either for or against any of the suggested schemes for altering the present system.

The preliminary studies of the past eight years have convinced the League Secretariat that in advocating calendar reform they are undertaking an important work for the good of the world. But these studies have also shown that the effort to correct the present irregular and unsatisfactory calendar and to substitute one which is regular, stable and comparable in its arrangement, calls for the most careful and comprehensive study, research and deliberation.

More than 200 different plans of calendar simplification have been submitted to the League. The June meeting of the Preparatory Committee rejected most of these as unpractical, and gave main consideration to two perpetual plans—the 12-month "equal-quarters" revision endorsed by Switzerland and advocated by The World Calendar Association, and the 13-month scheme as proposed by Moses B. Cotsworth and George Eastman.

These two plans, therefore, will be the ones on which attention will be focussed in October at the formal International Conference called by the League's Commission on Communications and Transit.

A conspicuous feature of the June preparatory meeting was the rôle played by the United States in the deliberations. Six delegates from America were in Geneva, three of them representing the 12-month plan and three representing the 13-month proposal. Dr. Charles F. Marvin, head of the U. S. Weather Bureau and an ardent 13-month supporter, was one of the 14 experts summoned by the League to act on the official Preparatory Committee, and after the public sittings had closed he was made chairman of a sub-committee to draft the report of the week's sessions. We feel sure from our pleasant contacts with Dr. Marvin during the conference that he made a sincere and whole-hearted effort to maintain an impartial and judicial attitude.

Nevertheless, it was fortunate that the United States was adequately represented on the side of a 12-month revision, for the facts and figures which we presented made it clear to the League Secretariat that the United States is by no means unanimous for the Eastman-Cotsworth scheme.

The report of the Preparatory Committee, in summarizing public opinion in 16 countries, does not indicate any preponderance of world-wide support for the 13-month proposal. The findings are based on reports received mainly from questionnaires, which were sent out in most cases to limited lists by "national committees" of unofficial character; the results, therefore, are generally no more "nationally" authoritative than those reported by the American Committee, which is headed by Mr. Eastman and composed almost entirely of supporters of the 13-month plan.

Taking these 16 reports, however, at their face value, it is interesting to note that only 6 of them favor the 13-month scheme. Belgium and Switzerland definitely endorse the 12-month revision, and Germany, Italy, Holland, Argentina and Hungary indicate a preference for the 12-month plan, but believe the time is not yet opportune for definite decision. The British Committee makes an extended report which commits its authors to nothing, and there are similarly inconclusive reports from Sweden and Colombia.*

The six endorsers of the 13-month plan are: Czechoslovakia, France, Poland, Portugal, Brazil and the East-

---

* The report from Colombia, although omitted in the printed report of the League Preparatory Committee, was included in an earlier "Summary" issued in mimeograph by the committee. It is in the form of a letter from the Ministry of Foreign Affairs, stating: "The Ministry hopes to receive further documents on these subjects in order that it may be enabled to form a clear idea as to the convenience, utility and expediency of this reform, of which it is not as yet convinced either from the economic or from the social standpoint. It is of opinion that any simplification in these matters, if inadequately considered, might produce results entirely contrary from every point of view to those desired."

man committee from the United States. The Brazilian report is oddly qualified as largely influenced by a traditional loyalty to Comte, a French savant who campaigned for the 13-month plan 50 years ago. The French report admits a woeful lack of information on the subject in France and urges an effective educational program in order to enlighten the public before any decision is reached. The Eastman report from the United States is the result of many years of energetic advocacy of the Cotsworth plan.

Our own presentation of the 12-month revision was made on the second day of the conference. Although we had already submitted formal reports of our activities to the Preparatory Committee in writing, we felt that it was wise to supplement these with a verbal summary of our findings regarding public opinion in America. We had found, through questionnaires, correspondence and other investigations of varied character, that there was a widespread support in America for an equal-quarter plan, possible only with a 12-month arrangement, and an equally widespread opposition to the 13-month proposal. The reception which we received from the Preparatory Committee and from the League Secretariat confirmed our conviction that personal representation was a necessary and effective method of bringing the American situation to their attention.

The Committee's public hearing was held on Tuesday, June 9, presided over by M. Djouritchitch, chairman of the Preparatory Committee and representative of Yugoslavia. He had the capable assistance, at his side, of M. Robert Haas, permanent secretary of the League Commission on Communications and Transit, and Miss Key-Rasmussen, associate of M. Haas.

The morning session was devoted mainly to religious opposition to calendar reform as presented by the Grand Rabbis of several countries and by spokesmen for the Seventh-Day Adventists. Their objections centered around the annual introduction of the last day in the year as an extra day and another extra day in leap years, outside the weekday sequence, which they opposed as breaking into the traditional regularity of their Sabbath. Members of the Preparatory Committee listened patiently and sympathetically to these speakers, although it had already been made clear that the League for the present desired to consider only the economic and social phases of the subject, leaving religious arguments to religious authorities. Four venerable Rabbis spoke with intense conviction and deep emotion, and two younger Adventists talked along similar lines. All those present felt a profound respect for their evident sincerity of purpose.

Religious support of calendar reform was voiced by Prof. Adolf Keller of Switzerland, who spoke as the Secretary General of the Universal Christian Council for Life and Work, embracing most of the Protestant denominations of the world. He endorsed the League's plan for a stabilized Easter and indicated that his organization would not oppose any calendar simplification that would serve the good of humanity.*

The afternoon session was given over to a description of three plans of calendar reform. The 12-month revision was discussed by the President of The World Calendar Association, the 13-month scheme by Mr. Cots-

---

* The World Calendar Association would like to stress the fact that if Easter is to be stabilized, yet separated from a general calendar reform, and if the calendar is not perpetual, the Easter-date will still "wander." Its "wanderings," however, will be restricted within a seven-day period.

worth, and a novel 10-month arrangement by Broughton Richmond of Singapore.

Mr. Richmond's division of the year into "quintals" or fifths, and all the complicated adjustments which this would necessitate, left his hearers puzzled. Fortunately typewritten copies of his address were available for the use of those who wished to study his plan.

Mr. Cotsworth's presentation of the 13-month scheme was lengthy, and he quoted extensively from pamphlets and articles published by his organization. His address was complicated by his desire to make reply to the rabbinical speakers of the morning session.

The address in advocacy of the 12-month revision by the President of The World Calendar Association had the earnest attention of the Committee, whose members were particularly impressed with the results of the Wilmington Chamber of Commerce questionnaire as indicating that the business opinion in America was more favorable to the 12-month plan than to the 13-month proposal.

With the close of the June meeting, there seemed to be no doubt in the minds of those who had attended these interesting sessions in Geneva that calendar reform was making progress in all parts of the world. The gathering of delegates from so many countries naturally emphasized the magnitude of any international undertaking for improvement in the present system, but there was a manifest spirit of cooperation which gave a distinct feeling of hopefulness.

There are, of course, difficulties to be overcome, for any important change in the calendar will call for changes and adjustments in governmental, social and religious life. This, however, has been the history of every great calendar reform. When the Julian system was adopted by the

Romans, the public had to adapt itself to alterations in many traditions and customs, holidays and anniversaries, but the benefits proved worth all they cost in sacrifice. Fifteen hundred years later, Pope Gregory XIII corrected the Julian errors, and there was another period of adjustment, complicated by religious controversy which restrained Protestant countries from accepting the Gregorian reforms for many generations. The improvement, however, eventually won on its merits and religious objections disappeared. During recent years the Chinese, Japanese, Greeks and Turks have made various sacrifices in their adoption of the western calendar, but the change has been fully justified.

The arguments of the Jewish Rabbis and their supporters from the Seventh-Day Adventists left a profound impression on their hearers at Geneva. While other religious groups have indicated willingness to support the "Year-End Day" and "Leap-Year Day" which are required by all systems of calendar reform in order to make the calendar perpetual, these two groups stand in opposition, at least for the time being.

But in the atmosphere of Geneva, it seems easy to believe that progress is inevitable. There is a lofty detachment in this "city of the League" that makes it easy to look back over history and realize that the old is ever yielding to the new, alike in government, economics and religion. When one contemplates the lives of the great religious leaders of the world from early history—Moses, Zoroaster, Buddha, Confucius, Jesus, Mohammed—one is impressed with the fact that they never hesitated to renounce old traditions, if thereby greater benefits could be secured for the good of man. They gave new interpretations to life and its needs and accepted change, all of which were inevitable in the forward-going march of progress. It is this spirit of progress which will steadily work to smooth out the objections of those who bring up religious obstacles to calendar reform.

Students of the calendar recognize and accept the year as the central unit of time-measurement with the week and month as subordinate. In accordance with this interpretation, the current proposals for reform supply the only means whereby the calendar can become perpetual, at the same time coinciding with a true astronomical year. These proposals favor a calendar of 364 days with the 365th day placed on a double Saturday or eighth day and the 366th day in leap years placed on another double Saturday, preferably in midsummer. In this way every year begins on the same day and date and the calendar becomes regular, orderly and comparable.

The question before the world today is this: Shall this change be made and this new interpretation be accepted so that man can use an all-round, universally workable calendar in his daily activities and social relationships?

Under the clear blue skies of Geneva, guided by leaders of the past and present, the answer seems very obvious. Calendar reform is another forward step in the progress of human life. Cooperation, international, secular and religious, is easier today than it was 350 years ago in the days of Pope Gregory.

V

INTERNATIONAL CONFERENCE

Address before Fourth General Conference on Communi-
cations and Transit of the League of Nations,
Geneva, October 12, 1931

THE opening day of this conference, October 12, marks the 439th anniversary of the discovery of America, whereby two distinct and mutually strange worlds became known to one another. On the same date, approximately four and a half centuries later, citizens of both the old and new worlds have assembled here before the League of Nations to discuss a common interest—calendar reform.

In this modern age the economic world leans more and more upon experience; experience depends more intensively upon statistical records; and statistics demand a better arrangement of time-units by which comparisons can be made between one period and another. Socially, too, there is need for greater ease and accuracy in time schedules.

It is for the purpose of exchanging views as to the best way of removing the admitted deficiencies of the Gregorian Calendar and of obtaining the essential requirements of a reformed calendar—comparability, stability and regularity—that we have come together here at Geneva in its historic atmosphere of friendship, goodwill and cooperation.

I have frequently been asked what aroused my interest in this reform, and why The World Calendar Association was organized when there was already functioning in the United States a National Committee which had received recognition from the League of Nations.

A little more than two years ago I attended a lecture on calendar simplification, which was my first introduction to the subject. The lecturer was an ardent advocate of the 13-month plan. His arguments, however, were to me disturbing and his reform-proposal drastic and confusing.

His disquieting address was still fresh in my mind when a few days later I read a letter in the *New York Times* wherein a correspondent opposed the 13-month plan and called attention to an alternative one, known to Europe, whereby the 12-month arrangement was retained, the quarters equalized and the calendar made perpetual by the use of Year-End Day and Leap-Year Day. To me the practicability of this plan was obvious, and as soon as I had leisure, I began to study the subject.

As my studies progressed I became conscious of four outstanding facts:

First, that the 13-month plan was unnecessarily extreme in its methods of correcting the faults of the present calendar.

Second, that the United States Committee on Calendar Simplification was unduly biased in its advocacy of the 13-month plan.

Third, that owing to this bias a poor presentation of a 12-month equal-quarter revision had been given to the American public.

Fourth, that persistent stressing of the advantages of the 13-month plan was creating a distorted picture in the minds of the American people.

From these facts I reached the conclusion that there was urgent need for a fair presentation in America of the 12-month equal-quarter year and that this would necessitate a movement organized independently of the existing Committee.

It was with reluctance that I reached this conclusion, for I believe in cooperation whenever possible. In this instance it might have seemed especially desirable, for Mr. Eastman and his associates had unselfishly done a great work in calling attention to the defects of the calendar. In their remedy, however, I felt that they had gone too far and that their plan could not possibly win world-acceptance. Their solution was one which would complicate rather than simplify.

The organization of The World Calendar Association, therefore, became a necessity, and it has been justified, I think, by the popular response which it has received. During the past six months its membership has reached a total of nearly 5,000 persons, representing every field of American life and activity. There are sections of members from education, transportation, communication, agriculture, business administration, banking, the law, medicine, the clergy, the press, public libraries, public service and so on.

The result of our entry into the reform movement has undoubtedly stimulated interest throughout the United States. Up to a year ago the so-called National Committee was almost the only voice which had been raised in our country, and it was natural, therefore, that most people thought of calendar reform and the 13-month plan as synonymous. I became convinced that a great majority of the public found the 13-month plan too drastic for their taste and, therefore, silently rejected all reform as impractical and unnecessary.

In our discussion here this week, we have the benefit of several years of pioneer work on behalf of calendar reform, which has enabled the League of Nations to reach certain definite conclusions. Your committee has eliminated many plans because they introduced new difficulties fully as serious as those which you are attempting to remedy. You have also removed from consideration the correction of certain admitted imperfections in the calendar as impossible of public acceptance; for example, changing the beginning of the year to the winter solstice.

The League has decided that any decision on religious questions is outside the scope of this conference and must be referred to authorities adequately representing the religious groups of the world.

The League's emphasis on a perpetual calendar has, of course, met with some objections. The World Calendar Association, however, recognizes and cannot stress too strongly the fact that the indispensable quality of any new calendar must be stability. Without the adoption of a perpetual calendar the year would still shift as heretofore, and certainly halfway measures of reform would not satisfy a public which is informed sufficiently to accept the idea of change.

In order to secure a perpetual calendar which does no violence to astronomical law and at the same time continues the seven-day week, two supplementary days, Year-End Day and Leap-Year Day, must be introduced. With their introduction, every year will coincide with the preceding and following ones. Thus comparability, stability and regularity are secured and all daily, weekly, monthly, yearly and centennial reckonings are simplified. The benefits of such an arrangement will be felt in every department of human endeavor throughout the world.

There also have been discussions in regard to the League's recommendations for stabilizing holidays. It appears to be the general opinion that national holidays should be left to each nation for adjustment. Complete uniformity among all nations in respect to holidays may not be possible, but if they were generally permitted to fall on Mondays it would greatly facilitate many fields of activity.

On one aspect of calendar reform there seems to be general agreement. The inconvenience of the present wandering Easter is recognized on all sides. I would like, however, to suggest that we who advocate calendar reform cannot be satisfied with the vague proposal to stabilize Easter without waiting for a perpetual calendar as such as Easter would still wander within a cycle of seven days. To secure a partial instalment of Calendar Reform of this kind would appear to me to be in the highest degree unfortunate, as it must inevitably prejudice the chances of removing the defects of the Calendar, now regarded as indisputable by all who have studied the subject. There can be no halfway in this matter. The whole question, of which the date of Easter is only a part, must be settled once and for all at the same time. It is 180 years since the Calendar was last reformed and it is not likely that we shall see two instalments of reform within our life-time. I would, therefore, adjure the Conference, if it accepts the principle of Calendar Reform, to regard the fixation of Easter as an integral part of the reform and not as a separate question outside it and preliminary to it.

As to the date upon which a fixed Easter should fall,

I am of opinion that this should be the subject of further discussion. There are arguments against April 15th, the date most generally favored, which it would be out of place to discuss here but to which I refer in a separate memorandum submitted to the Conference.*

I come now to the plan for a perpetual calendar. The principal faults which we are seeking to remedy are:

First, the present inequality of the length of months and quarters: and

Second, the failure of the days of the week and months to coincide in successive years.

May I call attention to the fact that the number of months in the Gregorian calendar has nothing whatever to do with its present irregularities for which a remedy is sought? In fact, the number 12 has so much to recommend it, including convenient divisibility, that any suggestion for change seems unwarranted and ill-considered.

The equal-quarter revision, known in the United States as The World Calendar, starts with the solid foundation of retaining every desirable feature of the present calendar, particularly and especially the division of the year into 12 months.

By giving these months a regular quota of days, and evenly apportioning the quarters of the year, all the re-

---

* In a perpetual calendar April 15 has been frequently mentioned as the date for the observance of Easter. But the report of the Preparatory Committee stresses the point that the 15th is an important date for the payment of rents. It is equally important as regards dividends, interest and taxes. And the disadvantages of Easter coming on such a business date is increased by the fact that the Easter holiday in many countries spreads over a period of three or even four days and would thus interfere seriously with business appointments and engagements. Furthermore, this date would introduce an alien note into the religious spirit of the holiday. The World Calendar Association has, therefore, recommended April 8, which is nearest to the historical date, as the more acceptable.

quired improvement and stability of the calendar is obtained with few changes, no inconveniences, no upheavals, no statistical confusions and no increased expenditures. A satisfactory uniformity is attained without losing a pleasing quality of variety.

The distinctive characteristic of this plan is its conformity with the four established units of time-measurement, the day, the week, the month, and the season or quarter. Four times during the year, at the end of each quarter, these units synchronize—the 91 days, the 13 weeks, the three months, and the seasons or quarter-divisions. This scientific and mathematical balance and order is vitally important.

As an illustration of its value, let us take a corporation composed of several departments, which function quite separately from one another, yet belong to and derive their existence from the parent company. There is, for instance, one department which deals with temporary workers whose wages are computed on a daily basis. There is another department in charge of permanent employees with financial operations based on the week as a unit. The shipping and transportation sections use the month for their records; while the major financing of the corporation, including dividends, bond interest and general reports, is computed on a quarterly basis. Relations with consumers fluctuate seasonally and therefore are figured in quarterly periods.

Every quarter—the perfect unit—directors of this corporation meet to study the reports from the different departments. Plans for the future are made accordingly, and financial statements are sent to share-holders based on the results of comparisons with previous periods.

In this corporation, then, we find several calendar units

in use in the various departments, each according to its needs emphasizing the day, the week, the month, the season or the quarter. But it is essential that these units shall synchronize. Otherwise the work is unduly complicated and a broad survey of the whole business is unobtainable.

Only under an equal-quarter calendar is such synchronization conveniently possible. The 13-month plan, by discarding quarterly units, would bring confusion into corporation accounting. But under the proposed 12-month division, all time-units would coincide with a perfection which has never been possible under the present calendar.

I have in mind another illustration, more homely and more intimate in its application. Let us suppose a family with four children. The youngest returns to the paternal home each evening after work; the next comes from a nearby city only at the end of the week. Another pays his visit to the family monthly; and the fourth returns at the end of each season. You will note that only under the equal-quarter calendar can the entire family circle be united at one time. And this happy event occurs four times every year.

These two illustrations indicate the perfect adaptability of the revised 12-month calendar to business and domestic life. Scientifically, it is not possible for us to disregard the seasons. Seasonal phenomena fill the world around us. They rule all our occupations. The quarterly period of seasonal succession imposes itself upon us as a unit of time with an authority no less absolute than the period of day or year, astronomically fixed and immutable. The World Calendar Association since its organization less than a year ago, has worked along lines laid down by the League of Nations, and has consistently used the League's terminology in defining its position and program, so that the plan which it is advocating would reconcile itself easily with those advocated by various Committees of other countries.

Even countries where no official committees exist have begun to show a keen interest in calendar reform. Japan is represented at the present conference, although it has no formal organization dealing with the subject. The news we have received from Japan indicates that the 13-month proposals are not popular there, and a communication which has just come to me from the Tokio office of the League of Nations indicates that there is more likelihood of the Japanese people supporting a 12-month plan.

The *Journal of Calendar Reform,* which we instituted as a forum for discussion, is mailed regularly to the various calendar committees of the different countries, and to other interested organizations and individuals throughout the world.

What then is the next step to be taken? Probably we shall agree that the world is not yet ready for reform. A vast amount of educational work is necessary before so decisive a step can expect to receive popular acceptance and approval.

But I think this Conference could go far to clarify the situation by making a definite pronouncement in support of a perpetual calendar. The point I would impress upon the Conference is this: that it is only by means of a perpetual calendar that we can obtain the desired qualities of comparability, stability and regularity.

With such a decision behind us, we shall be able to go forward on a firm foundation of accomplishment.

The 12-month calendar has the approval of so many centuries of usage that its origin is earlier than history.

It has its foundation in our oldest and most sacred traditions. The concluding chapter of the Christian Bible makes it an essential part of the allegory of the tree of life, and the Koran states that "twelve is the number of months with God."

VI

RESULTS OF CONFERENCE

*Report to members of the World Calendar Association on
the October 1931 meeting at the League of Nations*

IT IS a real pleasure to commend the wise action of
the League of Nations in handing calendar reform
back to the various governments and public opinions
for further study. It was generally recognized at the
Conference that the time is not favorable for such a great
change. General public opinion is not sufficiently informed upon the disadvantages the present calendar brings
to its users and the advantages to be gained from an improved and regulated plan. Intensive educational work
among all nations is needed.

Calendar reform is a world-movement that cannot be
stayed. It affects every individual, every home, community and nation. It touches social and economic life; agriculture, commerce, travel, education, science and religion.
It calls for increased effort to obtain a broader understanding of this important subject.

Upon only one phase of calendar reform could the
League Conference make a definite declaration. This was
the stabilization of Easter. It was endorsed in resolutions
to be submitted to religious and government authorities
for consideration and approval. The World Calendar Association supports this action of the League Conference
and will work wholeheartedly with the churches of Amer-

ica in an effort to make a stabilized Easter effective as soon
as possible. Of course, it is understood that Easter will
still shift from year to year but its shifting is reduced
to only seven days which is an improvement when compared to the thirty-five days as at present.

The report or "Survey" on calendar reform, approved
by the League Conference in October, states in effect that
for the first time public opinion as a whole has begun to
be in a position seriously to discuss the advantages and
drawbacks of the simplification of the Gregorian calendar.
For the first time, it has begun to be clear that it rests
with public opinion alone to take whatever decision is
considered advisable with regard to this reform. For the
first time, governments in general have been brought to
regard this question as one for official discussion and deliberation.

With regard to the report there are a few points which
call for clarification. It is noticeable that these points or
statements are carefully qualified, an indication they do
not express the convictions of a large number of delegates. These statements with their qualifications are likely
to be misunderstood by some readers. To clarify and to
interpret, then, is the aim of this paper.

One of these statements refers to "a mere equalization
of quarters." During the League Conference this was
rejected as insufficient revision. It refers to a suggested
plan of equalizing the quarters by merely transferring the
last day of August to the end of February. It does not
refer, at all, to the 12-month equal-quarter plan, based on
the 31, 30, 30 days within the quarters, which was consistently supported by a large number of delegates.

Another statement which needs clarification is the following: "It was pointed out that the 13-month calendar

was theoretically more perfect" rather than the 12-month revision. Five speakers, all of whom were in attendance as propagandists for the 13-month plan, were the only ones who expressed such an opinion. The practical and theoretical advantages of the 12-month revision, however, were repeatedly stressed by official delegates, who were without special partisanship or bias.

"It was suggested," the report notes, "that it would be possible to make appreciable improvements in the present calendar without introducing a perpetual calendar, by adopting a non-perpetual calendar of 13 months without supplementary days." The suggestion of a non-perpetual 13-month calendar was a concession by two 13-month advocates to the opposition raised at Geneva by representatives of two religious organizations, the Hebrews and Seventh-Day Adventists. These were the only observers present from religious groups, except the representative of the Church of England, who indicated that there was no objection from his church to calendar reform. Many of the important church leaders of Europe and America had previously indicated a similarly liberal attitude to that of the Church of England.

Certain religious groups and governments have opposed reforms in the past, only to accept them later on. Thus it was with the early Julian and later Gregorian calendar reforms, and thus it was with the adoption of Standard Time by Europe and America in the early eighties.

Perhaps it is not yet sufficiently realized by the opposition group that in the perpetual calendar plan the seven-day week is loyally upheld within the year. The last day, Year-End Day, placed on an extra Saturday at the end of each year, safeguards the week and protects the first day Sunday, and the seventh day Sabbath, within each year. The year is a specific unit of time. The day, week and month are parts of the year and they all begin their annual round together on the same day of every new year, January 1.

In regard to the sanctity of the Sabbath, Hebrew Scripture says: "The Sabbath is given into your hands; ye were not given over into her hands." Or in the familiar words in the Christian Gospel: "The Sabbath was made for man, and not man for the Sabbath."

Upon a vital issue of calendar reform—whether we are to have 12 or 13 months—Religion everywhere should devote its attention. The Old and the New Testament of the Bible abound with the number 12. The arrangement of the new 12-month calendar agrees with the prophetic city; and in the concluding chapter of the New Testament, one reads of the symbolic tree of life "which bare 12 manner of fruits and yielded her fruit every month." A little further on the reader is warned against adding or taking away one word of the prophecy of this final book. Religious leaders have ever been aware of the salient qualities of the number 12—balance, harmony, division—and because of this they have preserved to man the 12-month calendar. In the Koran, sacred book of the Moslems, there is this statement: "Twelve months is the number of months with God."

At Geneva the Turkish delegate raised no question of Moslem opposition to a change in the calendar on the ground of religion. Japan, follower of Buddhism and Shintoism, voiced no religious objections but definitely opposed a 13-month calendar while favoring improvement. Mahatma Gandhi, leader of the Hindus in India, expressed in a written statement his approval of reform and a 12-month plan.

Government delegates who expressed their opinions favoring a 12-month division were Switzerland, Japan, Italy, Netherlands, Greece, Germany, Irish Free State, and Danzig. Some of these favored the perpetual calendar; others did not. But M. Vasconcellos, president of the League Conference, in summarizing the discussions on this subject, declared that "as far as a reform is desired, the preference appears to be for a perpetual calendar."

One of the interesting points brought up in the report is the question of auxiliary calendars. "It was suggested" that it might be possible in due course to confer upon these auxiliary calendars a legal recognition "concurrently with the use of the ordinary calendar." It is decidedly questionable whether delegates at the League Conference desired to go so far as to give these calendars "official character." The mere suggestion of legalizing auxiliary calendars would be discouraged in most countries on the ground that they would complicate and not simplify the calendar. Auxiliary calendars may be used for accounting purposes in certain industries as at present, but to invite their increase or to give them "official character" would seem unwise to most governments.

The World Calendar Association places among its endeavors the advocacy of the League's program for a stabilized Easter. At the same time, the Association will continue its educational activities, which will aim to inform public opinion upon the disadvantages of the present calendar and the benefits to be derived from reform, for popular education in calendar revision is the immediate and pressing need. Toward these ends we will devote our efforts.

It is confidently believed that the ultimate choice of the public will be for the perpetual 12-month calendar. It has much to commend it. It retains the best in tradition; it recognizes natural laws and time-divisions; it accords with the majority of religions; it upholds the balance of time, and it keeps step with the march of progress.

VII

CALENDAR AND THE LAW

*Address before Committee on Commerce
of the American Bar Association
New York, April 12, 1932*

IN 1928 the American Bar Association first indicated its interest in calendar revision, asking the Committee on Commerce to study the subject from its legal and commercial aspects. A year later the Bar Association adopted a resolution requesting the United State government to participate in international conferences on calendar reform.

A significant fact on both occasions was that the Bar Association avoided endorsement of any particular plan, notwithstanding the efforts of an active group of 13-month advocates. The more moderate and reasonable plan for a revised 12-month equal-quarter calendar was then almost unknown in this country.

Last year, however, I had the pleasure of addressing your Committee in support of this plan, known in the United States as The World Calendar, showing how it would remedy the important defects of the present calendar without the upheaval which must accompany adoption of the 13-month proposal.

Your Committee, after giving the subject earnest consideration, decided last year to keep the question open until after the international conference which was to be held at Geneva in October. That conference has since taken place, and its proceedings marked a definite stage in the progress of calendar reform.

It was my privilege to attend the sessions at Geneva in October, as well as the earlier meetings there of the Preparatory Committee which mapped out the program for the international conference. A brief first-hand account of the accomplishments and results of that conference is of value.

Perhaps the most important action taken at Geneva was the weeding out of scores of impractical plans for calendar changes, which are now eliminated by international agreement.

Some of the rejected plans were: First, proposals advocating four long and eight short months, rejected "because the very perceptible inequality of the months would be extremely inconvenient from every point of view"; Second, plans proposing a calendar with an extra week every five or six years, rejected on the ground that they are "inferior to the existing calendar and cannot be considered at all"; Third, plans for a decimal system of time-measurement; Fourth, plans for a five, six or ten-day week; Fifth, plans for changing the date of the New Year; Sixth, plans proposing a mere equalization of the year by transferring the last day of August to the last day of February.

With these eliminations, the issue narrows itself to two principal plans for revision: The perpetual 13-month and the perpetual 12-month equal-quarter calendars.

At the October conference delegates from 44 nations assembled to exchange views on calendar reform. It was a noteworthy gathering, the first of its kind and scope in history. There was general agreement on the deficiencies of the present calendar; there was general agreement on the need for revision; but on the exact method to be adopted, there was not only an absence of agreement, but a feeling that the subject required further study, research and education before governments would be ready to commit themselves.

At Geneva the 13-month proposal lost significantly in strength between the meeting of the Preparatory Committeee in June and that of the International Conference in October. In June, six of the 14 members of the Preparatory Committee endorsed the 13-month plan. In October, however, with 44 nations represented, only two delegates, those of Canada and Yugoslavia, were in a position to commit their governments to the 13-month idea. Switzerland, Greece, Belgium, Italy and Holland expressed opposition to any 13-month proposal. The American delegate definitely stated that the United States government did not favor any particular plan. The Secretary of the British Parliamentary Committee declared emphatically that if the League of Nations should lend its support to a 13-month calendar, the sympathy of Great Britain would be irretrievably alienated. The Japanese delegate read an official statement that Japan would refuse any reform which would give the year 13 months.

The World Calendar, on the contrary, made friends at the sessions of the conference. Switzerland and Greece officially supported this plan, which was also approved by the representative of the British Parliamentary Committee. It had a large following among the delegates of Germany, Italy, France, Belgium, Holland and the Scandinavian countries. Mahatma Gandhi submitted a statement in which he explained: "As most of the Indian calendars are arranged on a 12-month basis, it would obviously be easier to meet on this common ground. I am in favor of such a calendar."

Since the October meeting, there have been additions to the ranks of the 12-month revisionists notably from Austria, China and Canada. The Austrian Minister in Switzerland has registered the opinion that it is of paramount importance to oppose strongly any idea of a 13-month calendar, which he terms an "extraordinary wildcat scheme." China, whose delegate at the October conference proposed a 13-month calendar invented by a Chinese scholar, has organized a national calendar committee, under the leadership of Dr. C. S. Yü, official astronomer at Nanking, who reports a majority of opinion in favor of The World Calendar; and, in Canada, the retiring president of the Royal Astronomical Society suggests the adoption by any leading nation of a 12-month plan as a very effective forward step in calendar reform, which is quite different from the view taken by the Canadian representative at Geneva. As for the United States, your Committee is already familiar with the increasingly wide public support for the same plan.

A considerable part of the report of the International Conference is devoted to the subject of the stabilization of Easter. I believe we are all in favor of this feature of calendar reform and fully realize the benefits it would bring, recognizing at the same time, however, that the matter is solely a religious one in our country. Because of this general acceptance the final solution regarding a fixed Easter date rests with the churches and may safely be left to their decision.

Summed up briefly, the Geneva report is in accord with the recommendation made to the conference by the World Calendar Association, namely, that the various governments should be allowed more time for study and education. The conviction was expressed that calendar reform is certainly desirable in principle, and that the present calendar is inadequate to the needs of modern economic and social life. But because of the world's present preoccupation with other matters and the need for more education, the League requested the governments to give calendar reform a more intensive study, and to stimulate public interest, before again taking up the matter in international conferences. This temporary delay is not a retreat for calendar reform but it is a spur to bring further intelligent action into the movement.

The need for educating the public has already been widely recognized, but the obstacle in the past has been the difficulty in obtaining suitable reference and research material. To meet this need, The World Calendar Association a year ago inaugurated the Journal of Calendar Reform, which supplies in easily accessible form certain basic historical facts and latest developments of the movement here as well as abroad.

Laying aside now the League's recommendations we can concentrate on the fundamental questions of calendar reform itself. Bearing in mind your Committee's stand in favor of calendar revision, let us briefly restate the defects of the present system so that we can get a clearer idea of what is desired in a new one.

A calendar that shifts from year to year, that constantly keeps one guessing on what weekday a date will fall this year, on what day it fell five years ago, or on what day it will come five years hence, is inconvenient and inefficient. Added to this difficulty is the unequal length of months,— for example, two successive summer months of 31 days, one winter month of only 28 days (29 in Leap Year). It is impossible to divide the year evenly, so that the length of quarters varies among 90, 91 and 92 days and there is a difference of 2 or 3 days between the half-year divisions. Comparability, so much desired in our modern age, is unattainable.

Wandering holidays add to the inconveniences. The present arrangement, in short, is disorderly, irregular and unreasonable.

The first objective in correcting the calendar is to bring it into the realm of law, order and harmony. The builders of calendars from the beginning did acknowledge astronomy and certain laws of mathematics. They did not sufficiently recognize, however, the vast system of the universe, in which there is developed an orderly and harmonious arrangement made up of many complex parts. With the awakening sense of understanding, a nicer regard for balance, variableness, order and stability, as evidenced by the cosmic law, is a necessity that must find its place in a calendar adequate for the present and future.

In how great a measure do the two plans agree with these fundamental requirements?

The International Fixed Calendar of 13 months is a disorganized arrangement in so far that it does not take the year as the principal unit. It gives the month the important place and so arranges that month that it agrees with the days and weeks. By this method, however, the calendar lacks divisibility; it eliminates the seasonal periods; it has no balance; it ignores a natural need for variation by its fixed monotony; it increases expenses; it annuls all historical data and statistical records of the past; and it complicates adjustment in its many drastic upheavals.

In contrast, The World Calendar of 12 months corrects

the defects of the old calendar with a minimum of changes. It achieves law, order and harmony in a simple manner. It takes the *year* as the principal calendar unit, arranging its divisions harmoniously so that at the end of every quarter, the days, weeks, months, season or quarter agree and the year with its perpetual feature is complete and stability is assured. This is only possible when the faithful number of 12 months is kept and calendar has even divisibility; when it acknowledges the seasons; has balance; harmonizes variety with regularity; conserves time, energy and expense; becomes comparable; reconciles the past with the present and makes adjustment easy and convenient. In a word, The World Calendar is an orderly and harmonious system of measuring time.

On the legal side Mr. George Gordon Battle has made a survey of those aspects of calendar reform which especially affect the courts and the practice of law. I would refer to Mr. Battle's findings as an important document for the use of your Committee in preparing any report which you may make to the Bar Association. Let me quote briefly a few of his statements:

"Proposals to reform the present calendar must necessarily attract the attention of the lawyer in active practice, for there is perhaps no one to whom the calendar is more important." He then gives numerous reasons why our present calendar adds one more difficulty to the many which confront the legal profession. He continues:

"The lawyer is interested in calendar reform because he is interested in the general welfare which it will stimulate. In this sense the point of view of the lawyer is necessarily broad for he sees with the eyes of all of his clients. His is the composite point of view of the manufacturer, the farmer, the banker, the dairyman, the broker, the storekeeper and all of the others with whose interests he is identified and whose legal welfare he attempts to safeguard. The whole community, producing, distributing, serving, consuming, measure and describe his profession. All of the benefits which a reformed calendar may be expected to contribute to the manufacturer, to the farmer, to the banker and to the others will, therefore, be of great and serious concern to the lawyer whose welfare and prosperity are identified with theirs."

In regard to the division of the year, Mr. Battle mentions one simple fact that is obvious to all. On the statute books of the State of New York the term "Year" means twelve months, the term "half-year" six months, and the term a "quarter of a year" three months. This definition appears to be a general interpretation and to change it would be a stupendous undertaking if not an impossible one.

And in advocating a plan, he concludes: "I believe most lawyers will favor The World Calendar. This plan appears to have all the advantages for which reform is sought and has no apparent disadvantages . . . on the contrary, it offers a simple perpetual system which may be achieved with very little change and without disadvantage."

Closely allied to the legal viewpoint on calendar reform is that of commerce and finance. H. Parker Willis, professor of banking at Columbia University and influential in the drafting of the Federal Reserve Act, has given us the conclusions of his studies and observations which you will find in the first volume of the Journal. Briefly summarized, he says:

"Standardization in the use of time has thus become desirable, and with standardization has come recognition of the inconvenience of the present arrangement of the calendar, and a feeling that if it could be placed on a more economic basis, there would be more uniformity of business practice and less wasteful management. Irregularities of the calendar are a disturbance to banking, finance, bookkeeping, and accounting, indeed to all the fundamental activities of business. But the fault in the situation is that there are proposals which would increase the inconvenience of the present arrangements, and instead of simplifying them, would render them more complex. This (13-month year) would be a backward kind of reform. A 12-month year is absolutely essential, for a change in the number of months in the year would throw out of gear our whole system. The economics of the case call for the fewest and most simple changes that are absolutely requisite, in order to eliminate the evils that have been found under the old system."

Gentlemen, the old system of the calendar is out-worn; it no longer fits our age. The time has come for individuals and especially for influential organizations and Committees like your own, who favor calendar reform, to concentrate earnestly on further constructive action.

In closing, may I suggest:

First, that it would be valuable if you could make a formal report on your deliberations, the publication of which after four years of observation and study would constitute an important basic and instructive contribution to the movement.

Second, that a decision for a definite plan of calendar would be highly desirable. It would have a far-reaching effect and would help to form and crystallize public opinion everywhere.

The probability exists that some one country will take the

courageous stand and legislate for a final calendar reform and plan. Legislative enactment in this direction would stimulate other governments and bring concrete results by the time the League of Nations again considers the subject. Thus by 1939, when the year under the present system falls on a Sunday, the new calendar may be inaugurated as the time-schedule for the world.

VIII

CALENDAR HISTORY

Address before the Sunrise Club,
New York, May 23, 1932

CHANGING the calendar is an increasingly important and absorbing question since the unsettled conditions in the economic and social world are forcing people to look for corrective measures of adjustment. In their studies and researches toward securing this end, the calendar is not escaping attention. We are discovering that this familiar measuring-rod, by which mankind has recorded past, present and future events, is a somewhat haphazard system, irregular and disorderly. In our exacting modern age, the shifting calendar is no longer adequate. And why? Because as a unit of measurement, the calendar is most inaccurate. In certain respects, it wanders in an indefinite way; months are irregular, quarters are unequal, years do not agree with each other. No year ever begins on the same day of the week as its predecessor, and the weekdays change their date from one year to the next. Holidays can fall on Sundays, at the beginning of the week, at the end of the week or in the middle. They break up the working-week with disastrous effects on the efficiency of our working life, our school-days and many other endeavors. As a result, our yearly, monthly and daily comparisons are complicated and often well-nigh impossible.

Then there is Easter, wandering from March 22 to April 25, over a gamut of 35 days, more than a month, seemingly never in the right place.

Altogether, then, there certainly is enough of a quality of looseness in our present system of time-reckoning to justify one in saying that our calendar leads us into a series of wild goose-chases every year. Who of us can tell without referring to the calendar on what day of the week Christmas falls this year? On what date Easter comes next year? How many Saturdays or Thursdays has June this summer?

All this disorder and uncertainty are disturbing, wasteful and inconvenient, not to mention their cost to our nervous energy and ease of mind.

One naturally wonders where these irregularities originated and why they have persisted so long. We begin to study the calendar, and forthwith are surprised to discover that it has never been a static thing, but is actually an evolutionary affair, which has been in process of development and change, even within comparatively recent times.

From primitive days to the present, the calendar has undergone many reforms. Earliest man in his reckonings made crude notches in trees, on poles or sticks, cut marks and signs in stone, built pyramids, mounds or totem poles, to indicate the passing of time. These registered important events in the life of his tribe, or marked extraordinary natural occurrences such as floods, droughts, storms or seasonal phenomena.

In the beginning, anthropologists tell us, the day was reckoned from sundown to sundown or from sunrise to sunrise. The moon, so full of mystery and fascinating charm, was the monthly clock and became man's first calendar. This was probably due to its noticeable changes in appearance. When these changes were found to occur in somewhat regular order, man believed he had found a basis for calculating time. We still call one of our principal time-units the moonth or month. For a slightly longer unit of measure, primitive man naturally used the seasonal periods, which manifest themselves in longer or shorter days, in wet or dry seasons or in cold or warm weather. These were significant sign posts, marking the annual progression of time in a cycle of seasons.

Numbers, too, became a necessity. Neolithic man, says H. G. Wells, learned to count, and fell under the spell of numbers. There are still primitive languages that have no word for any number above five, and even some which do not go above two. Neolithic man in the lands of his origin in Asia and Africa began to use tallies to count his possessions and to register the passage of the days or moons. Soon for him, numbers had a glamor all their own. He started wondering at the tri-angularity of three, and the squareness of four. He dis-covered that some numbers, like 12, were easily divided in all sorts of ways, and others, like 13, impossible. Twelve became a noble, generous and familiar number to him, and thirteen rather an outcast and disreputable one. Twelve moonths came to mean a year, and the sun's shadow served as a check on the irregular comparability between the lunar year and that represented by the seasons.

With awakening intelligence and better instruments at his command, man improved his calendar so that he could more accurately gauge the seasons and more easily tabu-late daily and yearly events. The movement of the sun in conjunction with the moon and stars and the earth-planet, was more carefully observed, and the seasons became increasingly important factors.

The highly civilized Egyptians perfected the seasonal year and adapted it accurately to the recurring agricultural blessings of the Nile's overflow. They based their calendar on the movement of the sun and thus were the first to adopt a purely solar calendar. Their measurements were a close approximation of the true length of the year, which they divided into the convenient 12-month periods which are now universal. Each of their months had 30 days, and the final balance of five days at the end of the year were handed over to the priests to be used for rites and festivals, which too often degenerated into orgies of dissipation and abuse. Their year commenced with the autumnal equinox.

This Egyptian solar calendar of ancient lineage, which seems to have been perfected more than 4,000 years before Christ, is the direct forefather of our present system.

Meanwhile, however, Rome began to rise as mistress of the western world. Its calendar development at first was independent, starting with a year of five lunar months, then a year of ten.

It is curious how many early calendars used five or ten as units of calculation. It was easy and natural for early man to count fives and tens on his fingers or toes. Indeed we all know people who instinctively count on their fingers when quick calculations are needed: thus persistent are instinctive habits which date back to the dawn of the human race.

But to return to Rome: In 713 B.C. the reformer, Numa Pompilius, undertook the difficult task of harmonizing the sun and the moon to the then current 10-month calendar. To accomplish this, he introduced two new months, Januarius and Februarius. The year began in March, and January and February were therefore the 11th and 12th months. It may not occur to everyone that the month of December means *tenth,* November *ninth,* October *eighth* and September *seventh.* Few of us ever pause to wonder why we call our twelfth month "ten."

Every calendar, if it is to serve the needs of mankind, must have a definite point for beginning its year. That starting point can conceivably be almost anywhere you please. Egotistic rulers have been prone to regard the universe as dating from their birth or their ascent to power; astronomers think the year should start with the winter solstice or the spring equinox; for many centuries the Church insisted that Easter should be the starting point. As for early man, the foundation of his reckonings came from the observation of rhythmical natural phenomena—the alternating of the seasons, the varying length of days determined by the sun, the recurrence of periodical winds and the rising and setting of the Pleiades.

Numa Pompilius picked March 25, the spring equinox, as the starting point of the Roman year and this system continued until 153 B.C. In fact, March 25 remained the accepted New Year's date in a great part of the world until comparatively recent times. England and America changed New Year's from March 25 to January 1 only 180 years ago, and the ecclesiastical year of the Church of England, as well as the fiscal year of the Bank of England, still observes the old custom and begins on March 25.

Our present calendar dates from Julius Caesar and came as an important result of his conquest of Egypt. By this time the official Roman New Year had been changed to January 1. When Caesar returned to Rome, he brought back with him the famous astronomer, Sosigenes, through whom he sought to acquire the remarkable scientific knowledge which had given Egypt its phenomenal agricultural success and wealth. This knowledge, largely astronomical, enabled the priests to predict the seasonal rise of the Nile by means of a calendar which was adapted perfectly to the needs of Egypt.

Caesar commissioned Sosigenes to perfect a calendar for Rome, similarly adapted to Roman needs. The old Roman lunar-solar calendar, with certain intercalated periods, had become a political tool in the hands of the priests and demagogues and this led to constant confusion. Caesar accomplished a noteworthy triumph when he reformed the old and untrustworthy calendar into an ordered, scientific solar time system.

The length of the year was established as exactly 365¼ days, divided into the standard 12 months, of which the lucky uneven months (the first, third, fifth, seventh, ninth and eleventh) had 31 days, and the alternating even or unlucky months 30 days each. February, the unpopular month set apart for the dead, had 30 days in leap years, and in other years was shortened to 29.

Owing to the fact that the year in previous calendars had begun on March 25, February was the last month and was traditionally dedicated to ceremonies of purification. It was regarded with fear and suspicion by the superstitious in an age when everybody was superstitious. Even the name *February* perpetuates this attitude of fear, for the word means literally "purification." It was human and natural, therefore, for the Romans to cut this month as short as they possibly could.

Julius Caesar established the leap year rule whereby every fourth year was given an extra day. On these periodical occasions, under the calendar as Caesar conceived it, February regained her rightful number of 30 days and became equal with the other even months. The Julian calendar was adopted in 46 B.C., and the year of transition was one of great confusion.

The Roman Senate, desiring to honor Julius for his achievement, named the lucky seventh month after him, which is now our July. Unfortunately for the new calendar, the assassination of Julius occurred a year later and his nephew, Augustus, came to the throne. The nephew was filled with such an exaggerated sense of self-esteem that he persuaded the Roman Senate to honor him also with a month to be named for him. Not willing to displease the Emperor, the Senators gave the name August to the month Sextilis. Lest he be offended at the unlucky shortness of his month, they lengthened August to 31 days, taking the extra day away from the already unpopular February. Then to avoid three successive 31-day months in the middle of the year, they took the 31st days from September and November and gave them to October and December. Thus the egotism of one man completely disrupted the ordered system planned by Julius Caesar, and left the world with a calendar in which the first quarter has 90 days, the second quarter 91 days, and the third and fourth quarters 92 days each. This is an irregularity which continues to complicate comparison of all quarterly statistics and reports.

After Augustus the calendar stood unchanged for three centuries, although among the people a new time-factor began to creep in with the gradual acceptance of Christianity. This new factor was the week, a time-unit unknown to the old Roman world, which was introduced by the Jewish civilization, based on the familiar Biblical story of the creation.

In the year 321 Constantine the Great abolished the old Roman division of the month into Kalends, Nones and Ides, and brought the seven-day week officially into the calendar, with Sunday as a universal day of rest. This innovation brought new complications into the Julian calendar and increased its irregularities enormously, for the week is not commensurate with the year or the month, and the weekdays therefore change their positions in the months and years in an endless confusion. From this time on, people were compelled to consult a written or printed table or calendar every time they wished to ascertain a date. Here indeed is one of the chief defects which calendar reform now hopes to remedy by making the calendar "perpetual," as in fact it was when designed by Caesar and Sosigenes.

It was in Constantine's time, too, that the confusing Easter date was added to calendar difficulties. The church, after prolonged argument, decided that Easter must be celebrated always on the Sunday after the first full moon following the equinoctial spring-date, March 21. Easter ever since has been a wandering festival, cause of untold complications to education, fashion, law, business, social and church life.

More than 1,600 years elapsed before another change in the calendar became imperative. The Julian year of 365 days and six hours was slightly longer than the actual solar year. The error was only 11 minutes and 14 seconds but with constant repetition, century by century, the error piled up, so that the Spring Equinox was steadily retrogressing into the winter season. It had fallen back from March 21 to March 11 when Pope Gregory XIII, with the advice of prominent astronomers, mathematicians and churchmen, approved the Gregorian reform of 1582.* Ten years of close study had been devoted to the subject. Leap year was corrected so that three leap days were omitted every 400 years. Ten days were dropped abruptly out of the calendar, so that the seasons were restored to their proper places,—the Spring Equinox was brought back to March 21. The beginning of the year was again officially set for January 1.

This Gregorian reform was adopted by Roman Catholic countries forthwith, but Protestant nations refused to accept the change for varying periods of time. Great Britain with her colonies held out for 170 years, finally adopting the Gregorian calendar in 1752. Because of this postponed action, England and America had to drop 11 days instead of 10. The change was a drastic and severe one, accompanied by riots in England and ignored by many of the American colonies. For fifty years after its adoption, the law courts were filled with legal wrangles resulting from it. Even so, the Gregorian reform failed to correct some of the most glaring and wasteful defects of the calendar.

To finish what the Gregorian reform left undone is the purpose of the present movement. In 1923, the League of Nations first gave this subject its serious consideration,

---

* On one of the Vatican buildings at Rome is a tower called The Tower of the Four Winds (*Torre dei quattro Venti*), not ordinarily open to visitors. In the sixteenth-century tower is a room still called the Calendar Room (*Sala del Calendario*). On the floor a meridian line was laid out and on fine days, a ray of sunlight, admitted through an aperature in the south wall, crossed the meridian line at apparent noon. The astronomer Ignazio Danti was thus enabled to demonstrate to Pope Gregory, in 1581, the ten-day dislocation between the true equinox and the calendar date.

at the request of the American group of the International
Chamber of Commerce. In 1927 the League approached
all governments, and suggested the formation of national
committees of inquiry and investigation. Last year
(1931) in October, the first International Conference on
Calendar Reform took place at Geneva with representatives from 44 nations. The results, while by no means
effecting an actual change, were nevertheless important.
These results were three: first, the elimination by international agreement of many impractical plans for calendar
changes, leaving for general discussion only the two
major proposals,—a perpetual 13-month plan, and the
perpetual equal-quarter 12-month revision, known in
America as The World Calendar; second, an agreement
giving universal approval to the stabilization of Easter,
with the suggestion of a fixed date; third, a concerted
opinion that calendar reform, while meritorious, requires
further study, research and education before governments
will be able to legislate for any definite plan.

The League of Nations made the significant observation that for the first time public opinion throughout the
world had begun to discuss seriously the advantages and
disadvantages of calendar simplification. For the first
time, it was clear that reform rested with public opinion;
and for the first time, governments in general have been
brought to regard this question as one for official discussion and deliberation.

So much then for the history of the calendar from its
inception to the present day. The next move forward is
for governments and peoples—governments like ours and
people like you and me—to interest themselves actively in
this movement. Once we have learned from history that
calendars have always changed with the changing times,

and that the demand for revision is natural and human, what shall we do toward improving the calendar?

To hold fast to the good features of the present calendar, and to make the fewest and simplest changes consistent with the desired improvement, is obviously the wisest policy, avoiding drastic upheavals.

Among the good features of our present system certainly are: first, the tested 12-month division, which keeps the year balanced and divisible; second, the natural recognition of the seasonal periods or quarters.

Can calendar reform be practical and effective upon these as a foundation? The new ideas which are demanded in a revised calendar are: first, the equalization of the half-years and quarters; second, the correction of the wandering tendency of week-days, making the calendar perpetual and stable.

To accomplish the desired results, it is necessary to make only seven changes. If you will refer to The World Calendar plan which you have before you, these changes will be immediately evident. The first is in February, to which two days are added. Then the 31st of March is given to April, and the 31st days of May and August are taken away to supply the two days needed for February. December 31 becomes the new "Year-End Day."

With these seven changes, every quarter becomes identical. Each quarter begins on Sunday and consists of one 31-day month, followed by two 30-day months. In the first quarter, January has 31 days, February and March, 30. In the second quarter, April has 31 days, May and June, 30; and the two remaining quarters follow in similar fashion.

This arrangement preserves not only the divisional quarterly and half periods of the year but brings to these a complete harmonization never yet secured in any calendar. For the 91 days, 13 weeks, 3 months, one quarter or one season agree at the end of every quarter; thus perfect mathematical comparability and balance are assured.

The conversion of dates from the old calendar to the new is simple. During six months of the year the dates between Sept. 1 and the following February 28 remain unaltered. Fifty per cent of the calendar stands as it was, and the remaining fifty per cent changes but slightly, never by more than two days.

The value of The World Calendar plan lies in the significant fact that it does not overdo the simplification or rationalization of the calendar. Too often there exists a tendency toward swinging from one extreme to another, so that the exaggerated shifting of our present calendar might cause too tight a binding of a new one. We shall naturally seek to avoid any such tendency. In nature, we observe that everything functions with an ordered variability. We notice this in the fundamental differences of the recurrent seasons, in the directional code represented by the compass and its four cardinal points, in the laws which govern the four winds that bring us the icy blasts from the north, the warm mellow breezes from the south, the storms and rain from the east and the clearing blue skies with fair weather from the west. The laws of nature are based on flexible regularity. This indispensable characteristic of variety is apparent in the system of astronomical laws that govern the solar system, the planets, the stars and the various forms of nebulae.

So The World Calendar retains a pleasing and natural quality of variability in its ordered arrangement. Man's weeks and months and seasons are bound to be slightly

different, just as the hours in his day vary, so that nine
A.M. is never three P.M. and six P.M is never midnight and
yet the day always contains 24 hours. So, too, is the
sequence of man's days. Both business man and school-
boy know the difference between a blue Monday, when
they begin their work, and a busy Friday, when they
complete their weekly tasks—between the happy holiday
mood of Saturday and the restful spirit of Sunday. Even
the nine digits of our numbers have each their own per-
sonality and an ordered variability. In the measurement
of time, order should be combined with variety. The
present calendar has too little of the first, and as to the
second—our present kind of variety is unreasonable and
incoherent.

A word of further explanation may be needed regarding the supplementary days by which The World Calendar
is made "perpetual," by which a given date of the year is
made always to fall on the same day of the week. Year-
End Day, the 365th and last day of the year, is placed on
another Saturday after December 30th, itself a Saturday.
Leap-Year Day, the accumulated fractional day that com-
poses the 366th day in leap years, is placed in midsummer on another extra Saturday after June 30th.

This perpetual calendar, with its two supplementary
days, may be likened to the system of Standard Time
which reconciles and balances the 24-hour day in various
parts of the world. We have all come to accept Standard
Time as natural, though it was adopted less than 50 years
ago. We think nothing of spending 25 or 23 hours in
the 24-hour day when we travel. All trans-Atlantic pas-
sengers and travellers between New York and Chicago or
points farther west, know well these slight differences in
the clock, which compel the advancement or retarding of

the hands of one's timepiece. If this familiar experience is so convenient for day-time, why should we find it any more difficult to accept a similar arrangement for year-time?

Under certain conditions, a whole day must be added to one's calculations when travelling across the International Date Line in the Pacific. As Robert Bridges poetically writes: "Whence who saileth westward will in his kalendar find a twin day." This added day harmonizes time around our terrestrial globe without proving in any way a serious inconvenience.

Similarly, the adoption of Year-End Day and Leap-Year Day will obviate the wandering looseness of our present time system and replace it with an ordered regularity.

Another interesting phase of calendar reform is the improvement suggested for more important holidays which are observed here and in other countries. Many people feel that holidays would be more beneficial to us if they could be made to fall as often as possible on a Monday. As the pace of our lives and occupations grows more intense, we feel the need for occasional rest-periods of more than a single day. Week-ends, supplemented by a Monday holiday, would mean two-and-a-half to three days of rest and recreation, and under a perpetual calendar most of our holidays can be brought into such a pattern, which should prove an economic advantage as well as a benefit to human health and spirits.

In The World Calendar, for instance, Year-End Day and Leap-Year Day are holidays which lengthen those week-ends pleasantly, the first at New Year, and the second in the heat of midsummer. Christmas, retaining its familiar date of December 25, falls on a Monday, without change, and conveniently lengthens the week-end. Labor Day and Memorial Day fall on Mondays also, and Thanksgiving Day might well be transferred to Monday, November 20. We must remember, you know, that this national festival has not always been proclaimed for the last Thursday in November. It has been celebrated on Tuesdays, for instance.

Washington's Birthday and Lincoln's Birthday might easily be combined into a single week-end observance. With the celebration of Washington Bicentennial this year, we have come to know that Washington was really born on February 11, and there is no reason why we should not celebrate that date. Washington did.

Other countries, which celebrate other holidays than ours, will similarly solve their problems, changing some of them and making exceptions with others as they find desirable. A list of the world's legal holidays shows that 289 different days are celebrated as holidays somewhere in the world. But under the improvements proposed by The World Calendar, there are only two of these holiday dates which will absolutely have to be changed. March 31, which disappears from the calendar, is observed as a holiday only in Siam, Uruguay and the Virgin Islands. August 31, which is similarly removed, is a holiday only in Holland and its colonies, being the birthday of Queen Wilhelmina. However, this holiday will be transferred to a different date when another ruler comes to the Dutch throne.

So much for the effect of calendar reform upon our holidays. Let us in closing consider briefly a few illustrations of the benefits of reform in our various activities of life.

Take the average family and its home life. The household budget is simplified because each year is comparable and the apportionment of money for each year and month becomes easier. Social and business dates can be more accurately planned and more readily remembered. Anniversary dates with their days become established and permanent. For the children, holidays, vacations and important events will carry greater significance. No longer need the walls of the home be littered up with printed calendars, for the calendar will be like the multiplication table,—carried in the mind of even the small children without effort.

For education, the faculties of schools, colleges and universities will be spared the present inconvenience of planning anew each year the class schedules, the vacations and the incidence of holidays.

For business and finance, the calculation and computation of accounts, interest, wages and dividends will be facilitated. Whether a firm's figures are kept by the hour, day, week, month, or quarter, makes no difference, for these various time-units unite and agree at the end of every quarter. Reports, statements, records are more conveniently assembled and referred to. Forecasts and plans for the future are more easily and accurately made.

For employees and wage earners, the new calendar will help in the daily round of work and relaxation. Wages will be more easily and fairly apportioned. There is no longer a strain of remembering days and dates, and holidays can be arranged to come always at week-end periods.

For science, the accuracy and regularity of The World Calendar is a valuable help in study and research, conforming more accurately to astronomical and natural laws.

For agriculture, the seasons will be more clearly defined, and reckonings facilitated. The 12-month equal-quarter plan is essential as it balances and makes more accurate the comparability of seasons with the standard periods of time. Comparisons, statistics, records and "lore" which are necessary equipment to aid the farmer in his work, can be utilized more conveniently. The seasons with the even quarters agree more easily, simplifying and making more accurate seasonal sowing and harvesting.

For the law, a perpetual stabilized calendar is equally valuable. Court calendars need no longer resort to those awkward circumlocutions about the "first Tuesday after the first Monday." Certainly this fact alone is an indication that our present shifting calendar is not keeping pace with modern needs. The World Calendar can easily reconcile past records with present and future ones.

For government, a perpetual calendar on an equal-quarter basis would help immeasurably. Records, statistics and comparisons are retained with the added advantage of an ordered calendar where dates and days are permanently established. The inaugural date March 4 * would always fall on Monday and the different election dates in the various states and national elections would be established. This obviously is a great convenience and would remove the present irregularities which are annoying and costly.

For transportation, as for the vast business of hotels, resorts and various amusements, a stabilized calendar will mean a great saving of energy, time and money.

In international relationships, with the increasing dependence of nations and peoples on one another, and with the closer contacts that come from modern transportation

* In the year that this address was given the change in the presidential inaugural date from March 4 to January 20 had not been made. The change was made effective in an Amendment to the Constitution and officially proclaimed by the Secretary of State, February 6, 1933.

and communication, an improved universal calendar will
bring increased cooperation and efficiency. Order, harmony, balance and stability in time-schedules will be of
world-wide benefit.

I think it can be shown that calendar reform will benefit every person, community and country. No disproportionate value will go to industry at the loss of labor; to
business at the expense of the consumer; to influential
leaders at the deprivation of the public; to one nation
rather than another. It is an improvement which in its
regularity and unity will contribute to the welfare of every
man, woman and child.

Now what would be the best procedure toward adopting
such a reformed calendar? I would suggest talking about
this reform whenever possible, encouraging private and
public discussions. We should realize the important fact
that this movement is for all people beyond any political,
sectional, partisan or national lines. Whenever public
opinion can be awakened, it will strengthen interest in
official Washington. Eventually our government, backed
by public approval, will officially endorse a definite plan
of calendar reform. By thus creating national, then international approval, the committee in the League of Nations
which is especially empowered to consider this question
internationally, will be better able to make concrete and
definite progress toward simultaneous adoption.

Will you do your part toward helping this movement?
We have seen that in our homes, business and country in
general, a revised 12-month calendar has everything to
commend it. It is practical, efficient, saving, convenient,
and agreeable. Its benefits cannot be measured and its
transition is so easy that it will slip into the world as
smoothly and as quietly as Standard Time did about 50

years ago. If I may predict, people will hardly know within a year's time after its adoption that any change at all has taken place—but they will be consciously or unconsciously enjoying its advantages.

IX

EASTER CONSIDERATIONS

An article in The Churchman, June 11, 1932

THIS year's unseasonable Easter (March 27) has stimulated the interest of people in the world-wide movement for the stabilization of the date of this important church festival.

The Prayer Book shows that Easter may come as early as March 22 and as late as April 25. The average date during the past century has been April 8 and the actual date of the Resurrection according to astronomers and historians was April 9, the ninety-ninth day of the year. All those interested in stabilizing the date agree that the Sunday nearest to April 9 should be chosen.

The League of Nations has been in communication with the various religious organizations on the general subject of fixing movable feasts. Within the next year it will request the opinion of religious authorities as to the stabilized Easter and its fixed date, leaving the decision to the churches.

Certainly, a permanent Easter date would be a great benefit to the churches and the public. It would simplify the church year by giving it always the same number of Epiphany and Trinity Sundays and regulating the dates of Ash Wednesday, Palm Sunday, Easter, Whitsunday, and other religious feast days. There would be no more early Lents and wandering Easters.

A curious fact is noticed this year in connection with
the early Easter date. All religious and secular organizations whose fiscal year ends the last day of March will
record in their reports of last year two Easters and in
the new year just begun, no Easter at all will be recorded.

The wandering quality of Easter is of course due to
the fact that many early Christians were Jews and associated it with the Jewish Passover, which was set according to the Jewish lunar calendar. Hence, the old method
of figuring Easter according to the vernal full moon persisted.

Everybody recognizes the inconvenience of a wandering Easter and the need for reform, but not everyone
realizes that similar difficulties exist in the calendar itself
and will call for revision. The unnecessary irregularities
of the present system are a constant inconvenience to
modern life with its manifold activities and a handicap
since one never knows upon what day of the week a given
date will fall in successive years. To establish order and
regularity is obviously needed.

There have been no serious objections to calendar reform save those rooted in inertia and a lack of information. The last general change was made by Pope Gregory
XIII and was adopted in America in 1752. The present
demand for revision is no innovation.

A reasonable form of revision, known as The World
Calendar, is being urged in many countries and has won
a large following from those who have seriously studied
the subject. Particularly it has found favor among people
who object to an earlier proposal for a 13-month calendar.

The 12-month year has stood the test of ages and
has behind it the sanction of convenience, usage, religion
and tradition. In its arrangement, balance and divisibility

are maintained.   To abandon the 12-month year is unthinkable.

Advocates of The World Calendar show how the 12-month year can be retained, yet so adjusted as to remove the annoying irregularities and inconveniences. This plan regulates the length of months and divides the year into four equal quarters, each of 91 days.

This totals 364 days.   The 365th day needed to complete the year is placed on an extra Saturday after December 30 and called Year-End Day.   This method always permits the first day of the year to be a Sunday so that every new year repeats exactly the preceding year.   The accumulated fractional day which makes the 366th day, Leap-Year Day, is placed on another extra Saturday in midsummer after June 30.   These two days are essential to the calendar if it is to be stabilized and conform to astronomical accuracy.   The wandering character of weekdays in the present system is eliminated.

The introduction of Year-End Day and Leap-Year Day is like the addition or subtraction of an extra hour at the end of a day when people journey across the continent or the Atlantic.   Thus, Standard Time may well be considered the forerunner of the perpetual calendar.

This earlier reform stabilized the 24-hour day throughout the world, notwithstanding the fact that travelers spend 25- or 23-hour days when covering great distances, and their time instrument, the watch, is advanced or retarded. This variation, caused by the sun's light shining upon different places on the earth at different times, does not interfere in the slightest degree with the even succession of the 24-hour day.   And, likewise, the smooth recurrences of the week in a perpetual calendar would not be disturbed by the adding of an extra day every year and another one in leap years. Moreover, these days, Year-End Day and Leap-Year Day are placed between weeks and considered as special days, thus the sanctity of the seven-day week is zealously upheld. No extra day breaks the sequence of the weekdays between Sunday and Saturday.

It is self-evident that a perpetual calendar will bring to time measurement a desirable regularity, stability and accuracy. Such a calendar follows the pattern of the universe, that basic system of order, and it is only reasonable that mankind should aim to achieve the same quality in the reckoning of time—for time and the universe are interrelated.

Now that the principle of the perpetual calendar is explained, let me briefly revert to the Easter date. The League of Nations suggests that Easter fall on the first Sunday after the second Saturday in April, which in both the perpetual 13-month and 12-month plans would be Sunday, April 15.

This date because of its use for mid-month financial reckonings acquires too materialistic an association and, furthermore, there are objections to Good Friday always falling on the thirteenth. In The World Calendar the second Sunday in April, the Sunday corresponding to April 9 of the Gregorian Calendar in the year of its adoption, 1939, and considered as the historical date,—is April 8, with Good Friday falling on April 6 and Whitsunday coming on May 26.

Of course, it is recognized in our country that a subject so essentially religious in character, as the stabilization of Easter and its regular date, is primarily a church matter. There is no doubt that Christian churches in the interest of the welfare of humanity will agree amicably on the matter. Toward that end religious leaders can exert tremendous influence in advocating a stabilized Easter and declaring for a specific Easter date, at the same time indicating their preference for a definite calendar plan. Messages from pulpit and pen will bring this movement nearer a realization.

X

CHURCHES AND THE CALENDAR

Address before the Universal Christian Council
Geneva, August 20, 1932

AT the Eisenach Conference in 1929 the Continuation Committee of the Life and Work Conference adopted a resolution in which it declared that the churches should contribute in making a judicious choice between the proposed systems on the simplification of the calendar. We are gathered here today to consider calendar reform.

Change is inevitable in our ever-moving world. The old invariably gives place to the new. What more logical conclusion might be deduced therefrom than that calendars, too, change with the passing of time? And alteration is beneficent, if in the process, consideration is given to both the past and the present by welding the best of the old with the best of new.

Nations are drawing closer together through modern means of communication by telephone, telegraph and radio; greater facility in travelling by land, sea and air; increasing intercourse in national and international trade; more general education among people; frequent international conferences; and the organization of the League of Nations. These benefits have been made possible, in a great measure, by abridging space and distance. And in the same degree, as the world becomes more closely linked in common interests and general welfare so, too, the need of reckoning time on a common basis becomes a necessity. Our present method of calculating time calls for adjustment.

Experience is daily showing us that the Gregorian calendar no longer meets the exacting requirements of our age. The shifting character of the calendar by which a person never knows from year to year what day a certain date will fall, the uneven divisions of the year and the unequal length of months are clogging the daily wheels of activity. Much time and labor are wasted in the search for calendars; in the arrangement of future dates for corporate meetings, legal appointments and social engagements; and in the fulfillment of financial obligations on specific days, when a date happens to fall on a Sunday or holiday. Secular and religious holidays wander in a most confusing and haphazard manner. Furthermore, comparability is impossible; assembling of statistical records is laborious; accounting is difficult and computing of interest is cumbersome. All these disadvantages impede the smooth flow of life, waste our money and time, and strain our nerves.

In the past, calendars were made and altered by priests and rulers with the aid of astronomy. The two calendars by which Christianity has recorded time are the Julian and the present Gregorian. The first was inaugurated by Julius Caesar as Pontifex Maximus, and the Gregorian reform was adopted under the leadership of Pope Gregory XIII. Partly because of tradition and partly because of the religious influence among people the churches should consider and weigh the subject of calendar reform. Humanity is closely allied together. Moreover calendar reform is an important matter to the churches, for the stability of movable feasts is dependent upon what kind of calendar reform will be accepted within the next few years.

The objective of revision is primarily to unite all nations upon a sounder and more effective system of reckoning time. In order to obtain the best calendar it should contain the following: Order by replacing disorder; regularity by removing irregularity; stability by eliminating shifting; balance by supplanting the present disproportionment; and equalization taking the place of inequalities.

I believe there is general agreement that calendar revision is necessary, but there exists a diversity of opinion upon the best type of calendar plan for world usage.

There is a group which favors a complete break with the past in advocating a perpetual plan of 13 months of 28 days each. With this arrangement the year loses its divisibility and lacks balance.

There is another increasingly large body of public opinion which advocates The World Calendar, a plan which holds to the familiar 12-month division. It arranges the calendar so that every quarter contains three months, 13 weeks or 91 days. Each month has 26 weekdays. By thus equalizing the quarters a harmony among the various units of the year is made possible. Every quarter or season, months, weeks and days agree. With this arrangement synchronization is achieved which was not possible before. The year is evenly divisible and well balanced.

One of the principal aims in calendar revision is to get a stabilized calendar whereby a given day of the month always falls on the same day of the week. This can only be accomplished by the use of supplementary days, Year-End Day and Leap-Year Day. By placing these days between weeks, the seven days in the week remain undisturbed and unbroken. The supplementary days are considered as extra Saturdays. It is generally conceded that this perpetual feature of the calendar is a necessary requirement to calendar reform.

The perpetual calendar which stabilizes the year may be compared to Standard Time which established the 24-hour day throughout the world. The fact that a traveller must either advance or retard his watch by one hour when he passes from one meridian zone to another does not interfere in the slightest degree with the succession of 24-hour days. Likewise the introduction of Year-End Day added to the 364-day year of 52 weeks would not interfere at all with the succession of years with the continuity of the seven-day week. It is placed after the completion of the 52 weeks and before the beginning of a new year. The adding of Year-End Day therefore every year and Leap-Year Day in leap years conforms to astronomical accuracy.

There is a factor of calendar reform which must be mentioned. The League of Nations has asked you to give your opinion on the stabilization of Easter. It seems obvious that this Council is hardly in a position to decide immediately upon so momentous a question, which affects not only all Christendom but also all peoples. May I impress upon you the fact that the whole subject of calendar reform includes Easter stabilization, and that the fixing of Easter is not a separate question? With this in mind, I offer a suggestion for your deliberation: that you submit the whole subject of calendar reform to your research department for intensive and unbiased study. This procedure is in keeping with your resolution of 1929, wherein the Continuation Committee announced that it was prepared to participate in future studies and discussions of this subject. By thus giving calendar reform the important study it requires, and by presenting a comprehensive report, through your research department, to the World Conference of Churches in 1935, the Conference will be in a far better position to judge and to choose a particular type of calendar revision and to decide upon a definite date for Easter.

In undertaking the study of reform, attention should be concentrated upon obtaining a balanced, ordered and regulated calendar which all nations and churches may readily accept. The transition can be made easy by joining the best of the old with the best of the new. If we succeed in approaching an even balance of the scale in our time-measurement we shall certainly have accomplished a good work. In planning a change of the calendar we may dwell on the words of the late poet-laureate, Robert Bridges: "Our stability is but balance." Thus we may cooperate in upholding a better equilibrium in the world.

I believe that the Universal Christian Council for Life and Work can and should have a large influence, to the great benefit of humanity, in securing a well-ordered arrangement of a calendar which can meet effectively the growing needs of our age.

XI

WORLD OPINION

*Address before the Committee on Commerce of the
American Bar Association, New York City,
April 11, 1933*

IN view of the fact that several new members have
joined your Committee, you will approve, I believe,
if I review briefly the present standing of calendar
reform in its relation to this Committee on Commerce.

The revision of the calendar was first referred to the
Committee five years ago. At that time it made a brief
report to the American Bar Association, reviewing the
history of the calendar and the general situation, and
asked permission to continue further its investigation of
the subject.

In the following year your Committee recommended to
the Bar Association that the United States participate in
international conferences and discussions upon the subject, and the Bar Association accordingly passed a resolution to that effect. The United States Government com-
plied with the request and ever since official American
delegates have been active in international meetings.

After the hearing in 1931 your Committee issued no
report. Because of the approaching International Conference which had been called by the League of Nations
for October, you decided to postpone the matter in order
to await the results of that conference.

Your Committee, however, had declared itself in favor of calendar reform. Your Secretary, Mr. Desvernine, in a letter of March 27, 1931, states: "Our Committee, as you know, has committed itself to calendar reform, without recommending any particular calendar. We will probably keep the question open until after the International Conference."

At your last meeting a year ago, your Committee considered the findings of the International Conference but, being confronted with a somewhat inconclusive report from Geneva, it deferred action until this year.

Probably all the members of your Committee will wish this year to take some definite action, at least to the extent of a progress report to the Bar Association. Your Chairman, in a letter dated December 14, wrote, "The time is approaching when the Commerce Committee will have to take a position with reference to the calendar reform to be recommended by it." In a later letter he said, "I hope and believe something will be done this year that will lead the American Bar Association to take a definite position in the matter of calendar reform."

Certainly your Committee, having long since declared itself for calendar reform, ought to be ready, after five years of study and deliberation, to move forward at least a few steps.

I come to you, of course, to urge the merits of the 12-month equal-quarter plan of revision, known in America as The World Calendar, and to oppose the 13-month proposal.

I do not appear before you merely in a personal or private capacity, but as president of The World Calendar Association which has 6500 members active in nearly every walk of life. Our Association publishes the quarterly

Journal of Calendar Reform, copies of which are already in the hands of the members of your Committee. As you know, the conclusion reached by our Association is that the simplest, easiest and most practical calendar to adopt is the one which retains the 12-month year.

Nor do we stand alone. The plan we advocate has the official support of the Swiss and Greek governments, and of important groups or organizations in England, France, Italy, Germany, Belgium, Scandinavia and other countries. In the minutes of the International Conference held at Geneva, where 44 countries were officially represented, you will agree there was a clearly defined sentiment in favor of the 12-month revision.

In America, official opinion is even more definite, particularly in the three government offices which are primarily concerned with questions of time. These three offices are the Time Division of the Bureau of Standards, the Bureau of Navigation of the Navy, and the Naval Observatory which regulates the Nation's clocks and watches, publishes the official Nautical Almanac and guards the safety of our ships and sea-going commerce.

The co-chief of the Division of Weights and Measures of the U. S. Bureau of Standards, Department of Commerce, is Mr. Henry W. Bearce, who is the authority to whom every official inquiry regarding time or the calendar is referred. He has recently published an exhaustive and scholarly study of calendar reform, in which he favors the 12-month revision and opposes the 13-month plan.

The head of the Bureau of Navigation of the Navy, Rear Admiral Frank B. Upham, is equally emphatic. He said, in a statement transmitted by cable to the Geneva meeting of the League of Nations: "My interest in the

12-month calendar advocated by The World Calendar Association prompted me to refer it to the Naval Observatory for comment on its merits from the point of view of that institution, the personnel of which are naval officers and astronomers. I am pleased to say that their comments are entirely favorable and they recommend its adoption. As compared with its one competitor, the 13-month calendar, it offers to astronomers and to mariners very practical advantages, none of which would be true of a 13-month calendar."

The superintendent of the U. S. Naval Observatory, Captain J. F. Hellweg, writes: "The Naval Observatory has approved very strongly The World Calendar. The benefits from this calendar are manifold and the disturbance with long established customs is the minimum."

Turning now from Washington to leaders of opinion in various trades and professions, we find the same point of view.

Speaking for banking, the internationally-known economist, H. Parker Willis, Professor of Banking at Columbia University, explains very clearly: "The 13-month year would be a backward kind of reform. A 12-month year is absolutely essential, for a change in the number of months in the year would throw out of gear our whole system. The economics of the case call for the fewest and most simple changes that are absolutely requisite, in order to eliminate the evils that have been found under the old system."

Speaking for business, the late William H. Blood, Vice-President of Stone and Webster, wrote, "Changes suggested by The World Calendar are few and easy of adoption. It provides a year which is susceptible of being divided into halves and quarters without splitting the

months, and by thus equalizing the halves and quarters
the difficulties encountered in business enterprises and statistical comparisons would be greatly decreased and the
labor lightened."

Speaking for agriculture, David Thibault, former editor of Modern Farming, who has extensively studied and
written on the calendar, says: "Undoubtedly The World
Calendar fits more closely the agricultural need. There
can be no doubt that the farmer will favor that system of
time reckoning which, while stabilizing and balancing the
calendar, still preserves the 12-month year and effects reform without too radical departure from the present system under which he has accumulated his store of seasonal
knowledge."

Speaking for education, Professor Charles C. Wylie,
Secretary of the University Association for the Study of
Calendar Reform, informs us: "Among educators a
strong majority favors calendar reform; and there is a
decided preference for the 12-month plan."

Speaking for aviation, the late Rear Admiral William
A. Moffett, chief of the Bureau of Aeronautics, made the
frank assertion that "the navigator wants a 12-month
year, because 12 is a more convenient factor for the computations in which he is interested." Admiral Moffett
concluded that a revised calendar is inevitable.

Speaking for astronomy, members of the International
Astronomical Union are practically unanimous in favor of
the 12-month revision as against a 13-month calendar.

Speaking for religion, the great non-Roman body,
known as the Universal Christian Council, in 1929 declared for calendar reform and voted that the churches
should participate in making a choice between the proposed systems. At present this Council is intensively

studying the subject with a view to reaching a decision at an early date.

The Roman Catholic Church is equally interested in the proposals. A Catholic viewpoint given by the foremost American Catholic authority on this subject, Father Edward S. Schwegler, is as follows: "It would be rather strange if the Church objected to calendar reform, for she herself has been one of the greatest and most radical calendar reformers in history." The great Catholic journal, *The Commonweal,* has editorially given its support to the 12-month plan; and says: "It is greatly to be desired that the question of calendar reform should not be allowed to rest again until it has been settled in a satisfactory manner."

Furthermore, from the Eastern countries, Mahatma Gandhi of India has declared himself in favor of a 12-month revision, while Japan, leading Buddhist country, has officially voiced its opposition to any 13-month plan. An Assyrian writer, George M. Lamsa, in discussing the religious aspects of calendar reform in the Near East states: "I am glad that the 13-month calendar has been proposed and is being actively propagandized. It will help the peoples of the Eastern World to accept the less radical changes proposed by the advocates of the 12-month equal-quarter calendar. Eastern inertia has got into the habit of opposing every change, but when two ways of change are offered, it is likely to oppose the extreme and accept the other." .

And in conclusion, speaking for the bar, George Gordon Battle believes that most lawyers will favor The World Calendar. "This plan," he says, "appears to have all the advantages for which reform is sought, and has no apparent disadvantages. It offers a simple and perpetual system which may be achieved with very little change."

These brief comments, selected from many, express clearly the overwhelming weight of opinion for a 12-month revision and against the 13-month plan.

The reasons which have convinced those who have compared the merits of the two plans are, in a few words, that The World Calendar of 12 months is the more simple, practical, economical, orderly and efficient method of remedying the defects of the old calendar. In comparison, the 13-month plan is revolutionary, awkward, confusing, impractical and costly. It accomplishes no important calendar need that is not fully achieved by the simpler revision.

It goes without saying that a 13-month calendar cannot be evenly divided into the quarterly and semi-annual periods that are so convenient and essential to the economic and scientific world. These divisions, in a 13-month calender, become fractional factors, requiring difficult and complicated tables for computations. The transitional period involved in the adoption of a 13-month year would be an era of confusion, and the disarrangement of statistics and historical records would be enormous. Comparison of present and past would become a matter of guesswork, owing to the displacement of the compared periods, caused by the introduction of a 13th month. The seasonal divisions also will undergo a dislocation in the general upheaval.

The increased cost of a 13-month calendar would be a serious item of expense in many directions. There would be an extra monthly closing of all accounts and tabulations, an 8 per cent increase in the number of billings and postage, 13 instead of 12 readings of meters, monthly rentals, and all other monthly operations in business, professions and homes. The legal complications involved would be enormous, particularly in the adjustment of contracts, rents, leases and interest payments, such adjustments opening up possibilities of fresh bargaining.

The only advantage claimed for the 13-month plan which is not possessed in equal degree by the 12-month revision, is that every month would be divisible into precisely four weeks. This emphasis on the week, however, is purchased at the sacrifice of the convenient quarterly and semi-annual divisions of the year, both of which have high importance in business, finance and social life.

Considerable emphasis has been placed by advocates of the 13-month calendar upon the adoption of a 4-week accounting period by several hundred business concerns, and it is held that their use of this accounting period is an argument for a 13-month calendar. The argument is a specious one, for it can be readily shown that any firm desiring to use a four-week accounting period can operate this scheme perfectly under the 12-month equal-quarter calendar. But even if the argument were valid, it might properly be pointed out that there are approximately 2,000,000 business concerns in the United States, and if 500 of them prefer to operate under a 13-month system, 1,999,500 prefer the 12-month system. The majority in favor of a 12-month calendar is numerically overwhelming.

There is another argument against the adoption of the 13-month plan which appears to me to be completely convincing and conclusive. The calendar is not merely a device invented by economists and accountants for measuring business units, comparing business records and tabulating business statistics. The calendar is a fact in human life, which must be applicable to the daily existence of men and women whatever their race, station or intelligence. Their whole life is encompassed and regulated by it; their daily living is ordered around it; their feelings, emotions and actions are inextricably tied up with it. Calendar reform must be regarded practically, in terms of the susceptibilities, conveniences and traditions of the human race. In this light, the 13-month calendar becomes an impossibility. By no stretch of the imagination can it obtain the background of comprehension and acceptance which would be necessary for its adoption.

The British have a characteristic way of expressing the purpose of calendar reform. They say that the end in view is to "tidy up" the present calendar with the least possible disturbance of the present practice. In terms of that definition, the 12-month equal-quarter calendar meets the need perfectly; the 13-month plan does not. The 12-month revision gives the required order and symmetry; the 13-month proposal over-reaches the goal. How many men or women would care to have their lives so rigidly ordered and so monotonously planned as is demanded by this mechanistic 13-month calendar, wherein every month in its structural form is fixed and dull? Excessive standardization is unpalatable, narrow and confining.

The 12-month equal-quarter plan has the superlative merit of involving a comparatively small change from the present system. The new calendar will glide into the old without any shock to business, with changes so slight as to be scarcely noticeable. Comparisons with the past will be as they are at present, while for the future there will be a new accuracy much to be desired.

The World Calendar is normal and sane in its revision. Its balance and well-apportioned arrangement are pleasing.

It retains the year's divisibility into halves, thirds, fourths and sixths. In its equal quarters all the complex calendrical units agree—the day, week, month and season or quarter. As an illustration of the valuable quality let us take a corporation, composed of several departments, which function quite separately from one another yet are essential parts of and belong to the corporation. There is, for instance, one department which deals with temporary workers whose wages are computed on a daily basis. There is another department in charge of permanent employees with financial operations based on the week as a unit. The shipping and transportation sections use the month for their records; while the major financing of the corporation, including dividends, bond interests and general reports, is computed on a quarterly basis. Relations with consumers fluctuate seasonally and therefore are figured in quarterly periods.

In this corporation, then, we find several calendar units in use among the different departments, each according to its special need. At every quarter these units come together, which facilitates the assembling and the studying of the quarterly, semi-annual or annual reports.

The World Calendar unites all the practical requirements for comparability and convenience. Whatever the accounting or financial system, whatever the space period used in statistics or research, this plan harmonizes the diverse methods and unifies them into a balanced, ordered system. Government, business and family budgets are simplified without any increase in accounting costs.

And it may accomplish something more in becoming a valuable adjunct in reestablishing more balanced and harmonious conditions in the world. Quoting from an address delivered by Owen D. Young before the Univer-

sity of Notre Dame, (June 1932) : "No permanency of
any trend can be guaranteed unless we have sound and
fair balance between all the units in our economic body.
In my opinion, it was our unbalanced condition which
caused our trouble."

The same trouble—unbalanced condition—exists in our
present unsatisfactory calendar. Only as we correct this
defect can we expect to secure a more perfect time-keeper.
The World Calendar accomplishes this admirably. It is
simple and practical, and it meets the requisites of balance,
comparability and stability. In its arrangement it harmonizes all its various units, and equalizes and retains the
divisibility of the year. All this is accomplished without
disturbing the essential form, a calendar of twelve months.

It is a strange series of historical mistakes and mis-
chances that has given us the erratic calendar which we
use today. Our chief need, of course, is the application
of a simple remedy that will restore to it the perpetual and
constant quality that it possessed under Julius Cæsar.
Pope Gregory, whose name our present system bears, recognized this requirement at the time of his calendar adjustment 400 years ago, but narrow traditionalism, mass
indifference and ignorance prevented the accomplishment
of a complete reform. Now, I think, the world is ready,
and the need for change is recognized and emphasized by
the rapid strides which have been made in transportation,
communication and the interdependence of nations. To
our generation is given the privilege of transmuting an
irregular, shifting and inconvenient calendar into a balanced, perpetual and simple one.

It would be too much, of course, to hope that there
would be nobody who would oppose basically and fundamentally any reform of the calendar. To such opposition,

however, we can only reply that change is inevitable in the forward march of progress, and that, in this spirit of progress, time will work its miracles and smooth out the objections of those who are inclined to oppose any change now. The World Calendar is so great an improvement over the existing system, and the transition from the old order to the new is so simple and easy, that after its adoption people will wonder why any objections to the reform were ever raised.

The most important innovation in calendar reform is the inauguration of the stabilizing day, the last 365th day to be known as Year-End Day. When regarded as a double Saturday, it offers to the world an added day of worship or of recreation. Considered in this light, the day has a high spiritual value. It becomes a holiday, or holy day, in the fullest and best sense of the word.

In conclusion, I should like to say a few words as to the practical procedure by which the nations expect to enact the change in our present calendar. It is essential that the new plan shall be put into effect in a year when there will be the minimum of transitional disturbance, and when the existing order of the days will be such as to maintain, during the transition, the utmost measure of chronological uniformity. Such a year, when January 1 comes on Sunday, happens to occur in 1939, and then not again until 1950. In other words, unless the improved calendar can be legislated for 1939, calendar reform will have to wait 11 years until 1950.

For this reason, supporters of calendar reform everywhere have fixed 1939 as their goal, believing that delay until 1950 would be a mistake and a misfortune.

Leadership in the international conference will naturally be expected to come from America, England, France, Germany, and Italy. It is our hope that the United States will take its full share in this leadership, just as it did in the international enactment of Standard Time, 50 years ago.

American opinion, I believe, is rapidly crystallizing in favor of The World Calendar. The same plan, under other names, has already received the official approval of certain European nations and the semi-official support of others. The Vatican is interested, and the Protestant churches are fully cooperative.

To secure official American action in the matter, active support of organizations like the American Bar Association is essential. The recommendation of your committee, endorsed and approved by the Bar Association in formal resolutions, will go far, I am sure, in advancing the adoption of this reform.

XII

INTERNATIONAL CHAMBER OF COMMERCE

Address before the American Delegation to the
Vienna Congress May 24, 1933

WHILE reading the various reports that have come to me from the International Chamber of Commerce, my attention has been challenged by the repeated emphasis which is placed upon four qualities—stability, balance, equality, moderation. If these fundamental principles are necessary in trade relations, in treaty making and revision, in transport questions, in monetary standards and in all other economic, social and international situations, they are also needed in our time-system, the calendar. The revision of the calendar belongs to the progress and spirit of our time and civilization, for the world cannot function effectively without revising the calendar.

It is amazing that we have tolerated and are still tolerating such a shifting and irregular calendar as ours. The years constantly change; each one is different. The days and dates never agree from year to year. January of last year differs from this year and will vary again next year. It will either have four or five Wednesdays, four or five Thursdays. All this complicates business. Accurate comparisons are not possible. Difficult and cumbersome tabulations and approximations must be daily resorted to in the financial and commercial world.

Then, too, the calendar is not evenly divisible into quarter and half years. There is a difference of one day in normal years between the first and second quarter, none in leap years; a difference of one day exists between the second and third quarter; whereas the third and fourth are alike. Thus the first half of the year is three days shorter than the second half and two days shorter in leap years. These inequalities are important factors in the economic field, easily leading to error and misinterpretations.

Days and dates constantly vary. July 1st may be a Wednesday, a Thursday, or a Saturday.

This leads to constant confusion. When important conferences are planned there is a scurrying for a calendar, and paper and pencil are hastily put to use in order to decipher upon what day a particular date will fall. And then there is added the exasperating question:—"Is it a leap year or not?" It is not unusual that errors occur in invitations and in the making of appointments. I have had the experience, which doubtless you have had also, when the day and date did not agree in the invitation. Wednesday, April 3, was not correct, and we wondered whether Wednesday, April 2, or Thursday, April 3, was meant. It is humorously said that a woman will always decide on the weekday and the man on the month-date in such a dilemma.

In educational circles the annual schedules in universities, colleges and schools provide the faculty with days of trial and difficulty because of the constant changeability of the calendar. There are many other similar instances that might be mentioned. In these few words I have tried to convey to you the ridiculous and unreasonable nature of our present calendar.

We are gathering at Vienna intent upon correcting economic conditions. Let us also try and improve our antiquated calendar, based on a system 2000 years old, which will more adequately meet the demands and requirements of our modern world.

As you have a plan of the new calendar before you, I shall not enter into details regarding its arrangement. I shall merely call your attention to the fact that The World Calendar attains perfect symmetry and is perpetual; every year the same. In every quarter the various calendrical units agree. No matter what the accounting system may be in your business or profession, no matter whether it is based on the day, week, month and season or quarter, they all come together four times a year. This synchronization facilitates the assembling, studying and comparing of reports and records. In arrangement this plan is balanced and perpetual. The results gained therefrom are obvious. The new calendar recognizes the seasons, comparisons are facilitated, changes are few, expenses are not increased for business and the consumer, holidays are stabilized, and the transition from the old to the new is made easy by the retention of the 12-month year.

In plan and in result The World Calendar coincides with the aims expressed in the four previously mentioned words;—stability, balance, equality, moderation.

Another plan proposed is the 13-month calendar, which is perhaps better known among you as the Eastman plan. One of the obvious disadvantages of this plan is that expenses in connection with the use of the calendar would be increased 8 per cent. Moreover, it involves a violent adjustment that is both excessive and wholly unnecessary. Custom, habits and tradition—the good with the bad—all are indiscriminately discarded.

The 13-month supporters claim that the calendar is primarily economic and necessary for the accountants and statisticians. What business really requires is fundamentally what the entire world requires—a calendar that is stabilized, regular and comparable from year to year. For this purpose the calendar must be perpetual, a quality attained in both the proposed plans—the 13-month and the 12-month revisions. Comparisons from year to year are more accurate than comparisons between months, which must take into account the seasonal changes and the varying number of holidays.

A calendar does not belong to one special group, nation or people. It must be universal in scope and application. To monopolize it for one particular industry and to limit its advantages to one field of activity is to shackle it. The overwhelming disadvantage of the 13-month is the fact that it ignores the seasons. The seasons are made a minor consideration, and in subordinating a factor so important to many trades and businesses this plan invites criticism for bias and partiality. The farmer must be recognized, for his products depend upon the seasons. So, too, the historian, navigator and families, they have all the same inalienable right to the calendar as has the industrialist and the financier. To take a narrow view of the calendar, no matter how advantageous it may be in a special instance, will create injustice and confusion to the many. The 13-month calendar is non-divisible, unbalanced and disproportionate in arrangement. It is intolerant in its demand for extreme changes.

But I do not wish to be controversial. My objective in attending the Vienna Congress is not to ask the Congress to reach a decision *now* regarding the merits of the two plans.

The paramount duty before us is expressed in the Memorandum and the Resolution, a copy of which you have all received. I am happy to tell you that this document has the approval of both groups of calendar reformers. Both organizations in America, the Fixed Calendar League and The World Calendar Association, deeply appreciate the consistent and constructive activities the International Chamber of Commerce has taken in regard to calendar reform. You have established a splendid record of which you may well feel proud. But our proposals continue to need your support and interest. The resolution which lies before you gives official acknowledgment to the League of Nations for the active participation it has taken in calendar reform; it expresses appreciation of the comprehensive way in which the League has handled the matter; and it officially requests the League to resubmit calendar reform at the next general conference of the Committee on Communications and Transit with a view to reaching a definite decision, so that calendar reform may be enacted in 1939.

I understand that such a resolution must be proposed by a representative of the American Section before the Resolution Committee of the International Chamber of Commerce. I believe I am justified in saying that the American Delegation favors such a resolution. I ask your active, moral and vocal support, so that the League of Nations may be informed and convinced that another International Conference on Calendar Reform is desirable and necessary.

The International Chamber of Commerce has been one of the world pioneers in calendar reform. Its interest has been consistent and constructive. It has established a splendid record, which assures its continuing support and interest.

To us then is given a remarkable opportunity to transmute a shifting, irregular and unsatisfactory calendar into an ordered, stabilized and convenient one. No one can gainsay its advantages. Our daily affairs of life would be greatly benefited with the introduction of a new calendar—based on order and stability, equality and balance—not only for ourselves but for future generations.

XIII

RELIGIOUS CONSIDERATIONS

Address before Executive Committee,
Universal Christian Council for Life and Work,
Novi Sad, Yugoslavia, September 12, 1933

LAST summer the Universal Christian Council for Life and Work adopted a resolution requesting the Research Department to undertake a comprehensive study on the question of a stabilized Easter and general calendar reform. In view of the communication submitted by the League of Nations to church authorities on the Easter question, the Easter subject received the first attention of the Research Department. The report on the "Churches and the Stabilization of Easter" is the result of such a study. It affords me the greatest pleasure to take this opportunity to express appreciation to Dr. Schonfeld and his assistants for their very informative and interesting piece of work and to the churches, members of the Universal Christian Council, for their wholehearted cooperation and support.

In connection with a stabilized Easter Day a few historical facts are of value at this time. In 1920 Lord Desborough introduced a bill before the House of Lords to establish Easter on the second Sunday in April. This Sunday was suggested because it most closely conformed to the actual Resurrection date, which according to the general opinion expressed by historians and astronomers occurred April 9th, 30 A.D., on the 99th day of the year. It was discovered, however, that the second Sunday in April in our Gregorian calendar would in certain years overlap with the observances of Passion Sunday and Annunciation Day. In order to avoid this difficulty the terminology was then changed to "the first Sunday after the second Saturday in April." This Sunday was adopted in the British Parliament Easter Bill of 1928 with the tacit understanding that it would not be put into operation until other countries and churches had also agreed to the change. It is surprising to note that in the deliberations on the stabilization of Easter before Parliament, calendar reform was not considered.

When the League of Nations in 1931 adopted the Easter Act, the only basis of discussion was the British Parliament Easter Bill which definitely influenced the League in its decision. The same Sunday was chosen by the League and in an official communication was submitted to governments and churches for their favorable consideration and approval.

Realizing, however, that both the British Parliament and the League of Nations did not give attention to the effect the choice of an Easter date would have on calendar reform, Dr. Cadman suggested that I, as President of The World Calendar Association, submit to the Universal Christian Council for Life and Work, a Memorandum on the date for a stabilized Easter, a copy of which, I believe, has been handed to you. Because of this fact I shall confine myself to the last page in re-emphasizing the disadvantages this suggested Easter date would have on the Christian world in a revised and perpetual calendar.

In both the two calendar plans under consideration by the League of Nations, the "first Sunday after the second

Saturday in April" falls on April 15. Now it is well
known that for common practical purposes, rents, wages,
insurance premiums, taxes and dividends are often paid on
the middle of the month so that this date would cause
serious difficulties, hardships and inconveniences to people who must fulfill these or other obligations. Because of
the holidays immediately preceding and following Easter
Sunday, these payments must be either advanced or postponed. To bring into the religious Easter feast, affairs
of money, would be regarded by most Christians as objec-
tionable and extremely distasteful. Thus they would de-
plore seeing the churches accept this date for the Easter
observance.

Furthermore, when Easter Sunday falls on April 15,
Good Friday invariably comes on Friday, April 13. As
stated in the Memorandum, this date would strongly tend
to an accentuation and encouragement of superstitious
influences which churches are ever trying to allay rather
than to foster.

With these disadvantages a serious problem might
confront the churches—namely that of combating an increasing materialistic and superstitious element brought
into a day preeminently spiritual in character and significance. I cannot emphasize this fact too strongly. In
reality, I am convinced if calendar reform had received its
due recognition, "the first Sunday after the second
Saturday in April" would never have been given serious
consideration. Such is the danger of separating two important features which should never have been separated,
for Easter stabilization and calendar reform are too
closely interrelated for division. Easter is a factor in and
not an independent part of calendar reform.

If we return to Lord Desborough's original suggestion

to place Easter on the second Sunday in April, the over-whelming disadvantages disappear. In both the proposed calendar plans this Sunday falls on April 8. In the 12-month equal-quarter revision, known as The World Calendar, April 8 falls as nearly as possible on the historical date April 9, and it would also come on the 99th day of the year (31, 30, 30 days plus 8). Neither would April 8 conflict with Passion Sunday, March 24, and Annunciation Day, March 25. This date is also pecul-iarly free from established financial transactions. The advantages of April 8, the second Sunday in April, for an established Easter Sunday are threefold:—first, as has been shown, it falls as nearly as possible on the historical date; second, it is free from unpleasant and otherwise alien associations; third, it thus heightens the spiritual significance of the Resurrection.

In the 13-month plan, however, April 8 has no his-torical significance. Because of this fact April 15 is preferred as it falls on the 99th day of the calendar (three times 28 plus 15) and by upholding this slight historicity, the 13-month group appears to be strangely indifferent to the grave defects contained in the date, April 15. These salient facts will, I am sure, impress the Executive Committee with the urgency and importance of studying calendar reform together with the stabilization of Easter, since it conscientiously desires to promote both the spir-itual and material welfare of man.

It requires both changes, then, to secure a regulated church calendar in the observance of feast days, many of which are fixed in relation to Easter. Furthermore the inconvenience of early Lents and late Easters disappears, and the church year is ordered by giving it the same number of Epiphany and Trinity Sundays and regulating

the dates of Ash Wednesday, Palm Sunday and Whitsunday (Pentecost). But of even greater importance is
the unification of feast days which can be observed by
churches simultaneously throughout Christendom.

This reform also offers the advantage that where
church budgets begin on April first, the variations of one
or two Easters or none at all in a fiscal year would disappear entirely and the budget would become simplified,
more accurate and comparable from year to year.

I would like to draw your attention to two points which
call for special emphasis in the report before you: First,
the majority of churches agree that no objections exist to
the stabilization of Easter, and second, this stabilization
of Easter is dependent on a general agreement to be
reached between Christian churches.

Upon this matter your organization can and should
have a wide influence in securing a well-ordered calendar
which can meet effectively the growing religious and secular needs of our age. And thus I am confident that the
Executive Committee, which is assembled here in Novi
Sad as guests of Bishop Ireneus, will prepare the way
and will find the method by which it can make an official
declaration, a year hence in 1934, for both the established
Easter Sunday and the choice of a particular calendar
plan.

Such an official declaration would empower your members to present it before their own respective churches and
to assist these in effecting the proper procedure by which
an established Easter Sunday, in harmony with calendar
reform, can be enacted by its member-churches in appropriate ways.

And in addition, when the government delegates reas-
semble at the League of Nations for further deliberation

on the subject of calendar reform, such an official declaration by the Executive Committee could render valuable aid to the delegates in their decision on this very important question—a question which concerns us all and toward which no one can afford to remain indifferent.

XIV

WHY REFORM?

Address before the Present Day Club,
Princeton, N. J., December 13, 1933

YOUR chairman's gracious introduction implies
that I have done a great deal of travelling on this
matter of calendar reform. That is quite true,
but if I had been told four years ago that I was to em-
bark on frequent journeys involving many thousands of
miles of travel by train, steamship and airplane I should
not have believed it. I should have been dumbfounded,
if in addition I had been told that such experiences as
these were waiting for me in connection with my work:
to address the League of Nations and attend other international conferences; to visit the Vatican City; to be a
guest at the palace of a Bishop of the Eastern Orthodox
Church; to have tea with a member of the House of
Commons on the historic terrace of the British Parliament; to discourse with a French Senator; to talk with
Mahatma Gandhi, and to meet a whole host of eminent
and interesting people on the subject of calendar reform. I
would not have believed it. I should have set it down as
a delightful fairy tale, just make-believe.

The developments in the three years since I entered seriously and actively into this movement have been so rapid
and so unexpected that I am still wondering how it all
came about. But when once you have put your hand to

the plough there is no turning back. The plough just
pulls you on and on and on until the work is done. And
that is exactly what has happened to me and will happen
to anyone that becomes intensely interested, body, mind
and soul, in any worthwhile cause for the good of mankind.

I have been asked how I first became interested in this
question of calendar reform to which I am devoting all
my efforts.

One of your members here today, my charming hostess
during my few days at Princeton, was practically a
participant of my conversion to calendar reform. While
a guest at the Lake Placid Club I attended a lecture by
the late Melvil Dewey in which he spoke of simplifying
life and mentioned three ways by which such simplification might be accomplished. First, he said, simplify the
complicated English spelling; second, introduce uniform
weights and measures; third, simplify the calendar on a
13-month basis.

It was the latter item which interested me most. Simplification of the calendar seemed sane and logical, but
a 13-month calendar aroused my resentment and awakened an inner perturbation because I instinctively felt
that 13 would never simplify but only complicate. It was
contrary to everything that I ever believed was simple.

A few days later I read a letter in the *New York Times,*
September 8, 1929, dealing with the same subject. The
writer severely opposed the 13-month plan and criticized
the propaganda of this plan to the exclusion of all others,
—thereby misleading the American public into believing
that the 13-month plan was the only existing proposal for
calendar reform. The writer closed with the definite
statement that Europe favored another proposal, known

as the 12-month equal-quarter plan, which he outlined briefly. I was instantly impressed with the superiority of this alternative, and forthwith decided to do what I could to make it better known. Thus my work on behalf of calendar revision began.

No organization of any kind suitable for the promotion of this type of calendar reform existed in America. There was a so-called "national committee" on calendar reform, but it was under the control of Mr. George Eastman and was devoted to the propagandizing of his proposed 13-month calendar. Through Mr. Eastman's influence, it had obtained a sort of half-hearted government recognition, which closed all official channels in Washington to any consideration of the more sensible proposal.

I discovered, however, that there were in the United States quite a number of well-informed and internationally-minded people who were distinctly disturbed by the absurdity of Mr. Eastman's 13-month calendar.

In the course of a few months, I consulted with a number of these people and they gave me encouragement in the organization of a modest association which would endeavor to show Europe and the world that America was not preponderantly in favor of the plan sponsored by the wealthy camera manufacturer.

Thus came about the organization of The World Calendar Association of America. In the beginning, our feeling was that the work would be confined to an educational and informational campaign in the United States. But within a very few months, international events swept us away from this nationalistic field, and we found ourselves taking an important part in a world movement with its center at the League of Nations.

I was surprised and somewhat perturbed at the rapidity

with which our modest little American organization was drafted by national groups supporting a similar plan into undertaking the leadership of an international movement to oppose the 13-month calendar. But we had begun, and were compelled to carry on.

The situation we faced was briefly this: a great international convention, called by the League of Nations, was impending. Something in the nature of an international agreement upon calendar reform was expected at this meeting. The advocates of a 13-month calendar, backed by Mr. Eastman's money and by his far-reaching commercial organization, had carefully and zealously built up a support for his proposal which seemed likely to overwhelm the delegates at the international convention.

Throughout Europe there was a general opposition to the 13-month plan and a general advocacy of the alternative 12-month equal-quarter proposal. But it had no central organization, and no promotional force such as that which was being provided by Mr. Eastman for his plan.

The European opponents of the 13-month calendar greeted our new Association with unfeigned satisfaction. Letters poured in, urging us to take the leadership at Geneva, promising us support.

We had only three or four months to work. But we had some very strong friends, and they were unanimous in the opinion that the leadership of an American group would be more effective than any leadership which a single European nation could undertake. One of the peculiarities of international politics is that because of the many national differences it is rather difficult for a single European nation to lead its neighbors successfully.

So we undertook the task. There was a preparatory

meeting in Geneva to draft a program for the forthcoming international conference. Our organization went to this preparatory meeting, established itself and did what could be done to see that our plan got fair recognition in the program and agenda. At the same time, we got acquainted with our friends and allies in Europe and laid plans for the most effective possible operation of united forces at the approaching conference.

Meanwhile in America, our Association had been making effective progress. We had enrolled several thousand members, had started our quarterly Journal to publish authoritative research on the whole subject of calendar reform, and had conducted questionnaires and studies to show convincingly to the League of Nations that the unanimous American support which Mr. Eastman claimed for his 13-month plan did not exist.

In due course the international conference met in Geneva, with delegates from 44 countries in attendance. For eight days it deliberated on the question of calendar reform. I was formally invited by the League of Nations, in my capacity as president of The World Calendar Association, to sit in the conference as an observer, and at the opening session the delegates did me the courtesy of asking me to be the first speaker introducing the 12-month plan.

Our main work, however, at this conference, was behind the scenes. There were delegates from 44 nations to be contacted and informed, as to the best way to cooperate and work together. The advocates of Mr. Eastman's 13-month plan were a compact body of delegates, under able leadership, ingenious and skilful. Our opposition had to be organized after the delegates were on the scene, its leadership created and its aims clarified and coordinated.

It would require much too long a time to tell you exactly how this was done. I need only to say for your information that our efforts were successful. The somewhat hastily organized group of 12-month allies succeeded in effectively blocking the well-laid schemes of the Eastman group. The final report of the conference was non-committal: in essence, it endorsed calendar reform without definitely recommending either our plan or the 13-month proposal. However, it weeded out nearly 200 other proposals, and ruled that the nations of the world would hereafter consider that calendar reform should involve only a choice between these two plans.

On behalf of the 12-month equal-quarter proposal, known as The World Calendar, much was accomplished. Europe and the League of Nations were convinced that America was by no means committed unanimously, or even generally, to Mr. Eastman's proposal. At the same time, there was a definite coordination on a common front of the various national organizations, strong and weak, which were actively supporting the 12-month plan. Many such organizations, in many countries, are now acting together, and the combination of their allied forces makes it certain, I believe, that no 13-month calendar can ever achieve an international success.

Since that time the 12-month revision of calendar reform has been moving forward, gaining many important converts. It is sympathetically viewed by many leaders at the Vatican; it has the complete support of the great Greek Orthodox Church; our own Protestant churches, in cooperation with the European Protestant churches, are engaged in a study of it, which is certain to have important results. International trade bodies, labor unions and other groups, are also gradually being won over to an appreciation of the benefits of a revision of the calendar.

Our work in America is going forward with that of Europe. I am emphasizing our European activities merely because they are more unusual and therefore perhaps more interesting to you than the ordinary routine of our work in our own country.

During the past summer I visited seven European countries in order to discuss the progress of The World Calendar with officials at the League of Nations, at the Vatican, and in various European capitals. I attended the meeting of the great Universal Christian Council in Yugoslavia, the convention of the International Chamber of Commerce in Vienna, and one committee meeting in Zurich where our proceedings were in three languages, flung helter-skelter across the council table in a bewildering babel. Everywhere I went, I found a growing interest in calendar reform and an increasing understanding of the advantages of The World Calendar as compared with the awkward, ill-balanced 13-month scheme.

We are bending all our energies now to an international effort which will make possible the adoption of the revised calendar in 1939. It is not yet clear as to whether this international effort will take place through the League of Nations, or in an independent convention such as that which adopted Standard Time 50 years ago. Whichever way it is done, our Association has performed a very essential service in clearing the ground of various misunderstandings and impediments that might have seriously clogged the machinery. We have been especially fortunate in getting the churches to take a constructive view, actually uniting them in a definite support for our plan of calendar reform.

I shall now go on to a brief outline of exactly what we mean by calendar reform and why it seems likely to prove important and beneficial to this modern world in which we live.

The changing of the calendar has an increasingly important and absorbing bearing on our modern and progressive world. The unsettled conditions in economic, social, national and international circles are forcing and challenging us all to look for corrective measures of adjustment everywhere. In the studies and researches toward securing these measures, the calendar naturally has received attention. For the calendar is a tabulated arrangement of days, weeks, months, seasons or quarters of a year by which man reckons daily affairs and registers annual events, and as such it is one of the strongest bonds for world unity. And this greater unity, this truer balance, and better equality and nicer proportion which are so needed in our daily activities, are fundamental characteristics of the calendar. To obtain a clearer knowledge and realization of the need for a stable, balanced, ordered and equalized calendar, a brief review of the history of time-reckoning is essential.

In studying the early history of the calendar we are surprised to discover that it has never been a static thing at all, as many of us might erroneously think. It is actually an evolutionary affair which has been in progress of development from the dawn of man to recent times. In fact, it is in process of change today.

Earliest man in his attempt to reckon time made crude notches in trees, on poles or sticks, cut marks and signs into stones, built pyramids, druid mounds or totem poles, all these to indicate the passing of time. These monuments sometimes marked important events in the life of his people or tribe, or they registered unusual natural occurrences such as floods, droughts, and storms.

Prehistoric man reckoned the day from either sundown to sunrise or from sunrise to sundown. The sun and the stars were man's first clock, and the moon, always fascinating and full of mystery, was man's first calendar. From the persistently variating moon came the word moonths or month. Twelve of these moon periods were reckoned as a year, for already man was falling under the spell of numbers as the English writer, H. G. Wells, tells us. Primitive man mused over the neat triangularity of three and the solid squareness of four. He discovered that some numbers like 12 were easily divided in all sorts of ways and others like 13 quite impossible; 12 became a noble, generous and familiar number to him, and 13 rather an outcast and disreputable one.

With awakening intelligence, patient observation and better instruments, man gradually improved the calendar so that he could more accurately gauge the seasons and more easily tabulate recurring events. The movements of the sun in conjunction with the moon, stars and our earth-planet were more carefully measured and observed.

The civilized Egyptians through their priesthood and astronomers perfected and first used a seasonal calendar, basing it on the sun. The period of time it takes the earth to revolve around the sun became their year, consisting of 365 and a fractional day. Their calendar year further contained the convenient 12-month division, but their months were all of an identical 30-day length. The remaining five days necessary to complete the year were placed at the year-end and used for religious rites and festivals. The Egyptians were the forefathers of our present solar calendar and their official adoption of it, in 4241 B.C., is the earliest dated event in history.

Among other nations, the Romans of the western world were using a lunar calendar which led to great confusion because the recurrences of the new moon do not coordinate with the solar cycle. Their original calendar of 10 months was increased to 12 months, but even so they had to insert an additional month at certain intervals, usually, dictated by priests and astronomers. After Julius Caesar conquered Egypt, he discovered the more simple, accurate and ordered Egyptian calendar and decided to adapt it to Roman needs with the help of their astronomer Sosigenes.

Thus came the Julian calendar, which is essentially what we use today. Julius adopted the familiar and convenient 12-month year. The odd months were given 31 days, the even ones, 30. By this method, the five year-end days of the Egyptians were evenly distributed.

Fully 350 years after Julius Caesar, in 325 A.D. under Constantine the Great, the seven-day week was introduced into the calendar, with Sunday as the Christian day of rest. This new feature brought an element of shifting because the year of 365 or 366 days cannot be divided into an exact number of weeks.

Gradually it was discovered that the calendar was getting out of step with the sun, owing to a slight error in the length of the year in the Julian Calendar. The beginning of spring, March 25, in this Roman Calendar, was found to fall on March 21 in 325 A.D. so that spring had retrograded into winter by four days and these days steadily increased so that by the time the 16th century came around spring was being observed on March 11.

This absurd situation was corrected by Pope Gregory who, being a religious man, accepted March 21 as the beginning of spring, in commemoration of the meeting of the Council of Nicea. He issued a bull whereby ten days were imperiously dropped from the calendar. He also revised the leap year rule to a more perfect scientific accuracy. In the year 1582 when his revision was adopted, October 4 was followed by October 15.

The Gregorian reform was accepted immediately by Catholic countries, but Great Britain and America waited 170 years before they accepted it in 1752 when 11 days had to be wiped out. We changed our calendar during Washington's lifetime.

All this reforming is so close to our own time that we are made aware of the fact that changing the calendar is not sacrilegious nor unusual. It is a natural human desire to improve an unsatisfactory system. Thus it becomes our duty and prerogative today to correct our present inconstant, irregular and inconvenient calendar, bequeathed to us by an ambitious Roman, into an ordered, equal, constant and balanced system, more perfect and more fitting to our time and age.

How can we perfect and improve the calendar? Evidently the wisest and sanest policy to pursue is to hold fast to the good features of the present system and remove the bad. Among the good features are the tested 12-month arrangement which keeps the year balanced and divisible; the recognition of the seasonal periods and quarter divisions; and the holding of the existing chronological and historical order as far as this is possible. Among the bad features to be corrected are the constant changeability of the weekdays, the unequal length of months, quarters and half-years, and lack of comparability among the various time units of the calendar.

Our guide in effecting this reform is naturally mathematics. Everyone recognizes that the year is the sum total of the different time units. In fact the year *is* the calendar. Our great difficulty, however, is that a year of 365¼ days is not exactly divisible into seven-day weeks. Scientists have admirably solved the perplexing problem. They suggest the new calendar on a basis of 364 days, which number is divisible in many convenient ways. It gives exactly 52 weeks, while at the same time 12 months, four seasons and the four quarters are all divisible within the 364-day. As to the 365th day and the occasional 366th leap day, a way of adding them to the year was devised by an Italian priest, Abbé Mastrofini, exactly 100 years ago. He conceived the plan of placing these two days as "extra" days in the calendar. They are to be called Year-End Day and Leap-Year Day, considered as holidays and placed on extra Saturdays. Their position in The World Calendar is as follows: Year-End Day at the end of every year and Leap-Year Day at the end of June in leap years.

In the new calendar, every year is exactly the same. In fact, every quarter is exactly the same, year after year. The calendar becomes so simple that it can be committed to memory by children exactly as they almost unconsciously learn the alphabet.

Each quarter begins on Sunday, and ends on Saturday. The first month of each quarter has 31 days, the second and third months have 30 days each. Each month has exactly the same number of weekdays—26.

Thus the calendar, which is our most important unit of measure, becomes as simple as a footrule or a yardstick. Never again will it be necessary for men and women to be annoyed by the necessity of consulting a wall-calendar or a desk-calendar every time they put down a date.

The overwhelming argument for calendar reform is exactly this,—that our most-used unit of measurement surely ought to be as simple as it can possibly be made. The irregularities of the present calendar are due to a long series of historical accidents, perversions and expressions of personal vanity. They have long been recognized, but it was difficult to correct them in earlier times because many different calendars were in use by various nations and races. The disordered arrangement can be corrected now more easily, because all the nations of the world have at last come to use—at least for civil and official purposes—the same calendar.

We, as women, are keenly aware that at the present time we have a different calendar every year. Every January 1st, we have to throw away last year's calendar and buy a new one. How foolish we would feel if every year on January 1st we had to throw away our last year's clocks and watches, our tape measures and our kitchen scales, so that we could install clocks with new and different hours, tape measures with a different arrangement of inches, and scales with a different set of pounds and ounces!

That, of course, is exactly how our present calendar works. The cost in human annoyance, labor, inconvenience, and even money, must be considerable.

And it can all be so easily corrected. The World Calendar, as shown in the chart, gives us the new and perpetual calendar. A given day of the month will always fall on the same day of the week. Christmas, the 25th of December, will always be Monday. New Year's, January 1st, will always fall on Sunday, the first day of the week in the new year. The working year will always begin with Monday, January 2nd.

An interesting feature of the new calendar is that it

will enable each nation to stabilize its national holidays, so that holidays will mainly fall on week-ends. Holidays are beneficial mainly as extra periods of rest and recreation,—how much more beneficial they will be if they are always arranged so that they mean an extended week-end, giving three days of rest and recreation—Saturday, Sunday and Monday. Lengthened week-ends will greatly ease the strain of the business world, bring enjoyment to the vacational periods, to schools and universities, encourage wholesome recreational pursuits and add to the general welfare and happiness of family life.

And in the economic world, with a five-day week certainly coming to be an accepted thing, the holiday week-end becomes an actual necessity,—because a holiday in the middle of a five-day week not only hinders efficient work but is a very expensive proposition. In fact, I believe a holiday in the middle of a five-day week would become a mere apology for the real thing less important than the ordinary week-end and therefore likely to be resented by everyone.

We are all coming to appreciate that the economic difficulties of the recent depression, unemployment and general breakdown of prosperity were caused by over-specialization in one direction at the expense of others. This resulted in a lack of equilibrium, the disastrous effects of which are still upon us. The recovery program is trying desperately to curb this unwholesome situation by introducing more balanced conditions into our daily affairs so that a greater cooperation and harmony will ensue.

It is recognized, of course, that success of such a program is naturally slow. It cannot be forced; neither can the public be coerced into accepting it. In this connection **calendar reform**, an essential part of the new era, may prove a very valuable ally toward establishing a more balanced, equable and ordered condition in the world. But the revised calendar must contain the same desirable qualities of balance, equality and stability.

In my travels and interviews at home and abroad, I found everywhere an awakening interest in calendar reform and a trend to the 12-month revision. Personal preferences were generally for the 12-month plan, for the typical man and woman dislike the drastic and extreme 13-month calendar.

There are a few business organizations which are keeping their books on a four-week accounting system for reasons of convenience and expediency in one department or another. But when considering a world proposition for world acceptance, I discovered little tendency on the part of leaders or thinkers to come out boldly and openly for the 13-month calendar plan.

In the churches, there is a growing desire for calendar reform and a sympathetic understanding of its aims, coupled with willingness to study and work for its success. At the great world conference of religions recently held at Novi Sad, where I had the honor of being the third woman ever to be invited as a guest in the Bishop's Palace, the attitude was one of cordial cooperation. The delegates emphasized the great value of a universal calendar in the religious world. A stabilized Easter, they declared, which could be observed by all Christians on the same day, would exert a strong force for church unity. The bishops, archbishops and patriarchs of the Eastern Church whom I was privileged to meet in the discussion of the subject, were decidedly interested. Their interest is even keener than that of the western churches, for the orthodox church still functions under two separate calendars. In Yugoslavia, the country I was visiting, and in Poland, Hungary and Jerusalem, the old Julian calendar is still used, whereas the other orthodox countries have officially adopted the Gregorian system. The orthodox leaders are of the firm opinion that no 13-month calendar would ever be accepted by their people. They insist that the 12-month division must remain in any reform.

In talking with members of the various European calendar committees and with international leaders at Geneva, one realizes the importance of considering calendar reform from the world angle and not from any selfish national point of view. Of course, individual nations can and should do their part in paving the way for international acceptance of one reform or another at the next international conference before the League of Nations. To this end official, non-official, public and private activities are important in order to centralize and vocalize public opinion on the matter. For public opinion is not as yet sufficiently informed or organized. The average man or woman lacks the proper knowledge and fails to comprehend the importance and value of the proposed revision. Every one of us can help to meet this situation in a larger or lesser way.

Woman's opinion exerts a powerful influence on national and international affairs and when mustered for The World Calendar it can quickly and definitely advance the cause. I sincerely hope I am leaving with you a keen desire to take every opportunity to talk about it, to speak for it, to write in its behalf and to work for its acceptance. Success in calendar reform, as in any other worthwhile cause, is only obtained through the enthusiasm and zeal of many individuals.

XV

SOCIAL NEEDS

Address before the Literary Vespers
January 26, 1934

AT the request of the chairman of these well-known Literary Vespers, I have come here this afternoon to tell you something about the world-wide movement for calendar reform. When we speak of calendar reform some of you may think I am about to advocate the 13-month calendar because this 13-month plan has been publicised in the past few years. But I am opposed to any 13-month plan and advocate a much simpler and more consistent form of the calendar. In fact, I have devoted several years and a great deal of energy to combating this unbalanced, awkward, fractional and non-divisible plan. I advocate the familiar 12 months, rearranging the length of the months in a more equal manner. This plan, known in America as The World Calendar, has gained greater favor not only here but also in other countries, not only with governments and business organizations but also with churches.

The Literary Vespers are eminently successful in bringing into our every-day physical existence the cultural and spiritual values of life, thereby creating a better balance within us. In advocating calendar reform it is necessary to establish a better balance :— a regular order and permanent regularity, which is so characteristic of our clocks and watches. For both the calendar and the clock deal with time and both should be consistent in the balanced and equal arrangement.

Just imagine the confusion, labor, annoyance and money, if every January first we would have to buy new clocks and watches with a different arrangement of hours and minutes. And yet, that is exactly what we are doing with the calendar. Every year we are compelled to use a new one. There are fourteen different calendars and twenty-eight different months with which we reckon in no ordered rotation.

The calendar is never the same from year to year. Successive years never begin on the same day of the week. Certain dates fall on different weekdays, and months have not the same number of Mondays or Tuesdays or Wednesdays. January may have five Sundays in one year and the next, four Sundays and five Mondays.

And in addition to these inconvenient changes are the irregular length of months—28, 29, 30, 31—impossible to remember without the familiar nursery rhyme, "Thirty days has September, April, June and November." What would we do without this old jingle to help us with our intricate calendar? There are seven months of 31 days, four of 30, and one of 28 and sometimes 29. The uneven distribution of days to the months results in uneven quarter and half-year divisions. All of which causes annoying difficulties in our economic and social affairs.

For example: Universities, colleges and schools must annually rearrange their entire study schedule, activities and vacations; businesses are inconvenienced with a different number of Thursdays or Saturdays in the varying months, thus bringing about unbalanced conditions; finance must furnish long tabulations of figures in order to obtain the correct interest payments to be paid on investments and loans; statistics must also make adjustments in compiling accurate data between the irregular months and varying years, which are not comparable.

In the social world we are familiar with the errors made between the days of the months and the weekdays for invitations and engagements. And vacations, too, are troublesome to arrange. In the field of amusements, there are certain difficulties in arranging dates for lectures, exhibitions, concerts and opening nights for the theatre. These few facts are sufficient to indicate there are defects in our present calendar system.

But how may we remove these faults? The irregularities of the calendar and its shifting characteristics can be simply and easily remedied. The World Calendar, the 12-month equal-quarter revision, under consideration by the League of Nations and supported by large groups of thinking people in every country in the world does not involve strain or upheaval. With comparatively few changes the old calendar can be converted into the new; every inefficiency of the present calendar can be corrected and the new revision will meet perfectly the needs of modern times.

The outstanding innovation in this plan is to set aside the 365th day, the last day of the year, and to call it Year-End Day. This day is placed on a double or extra Saturday and stabilizes the calendar, making it perpetual. Every year begins on Sunday, January 1st.

In the occasional leap years, the leap day is similarly treated. February 29 in the present Gregorian calendar is transferred to the middle of summer and placed between June and July. It is considered as another double Saturday

and called Leap-Year Day. Thus July 1st will always fall
on Sunday, as in common years.

The 364-day year, by this method, is divisible into
equal half and quarter divisions, exactly like the even
half and quarter hours of the clock. The quarter division
of the calendar becomes an even 91 days, an even 13 weeks,
a completed three months, making one season or quarter,
which is repeated in the remaining three quarters. Every
quarter begins on a Sunday and ends on Saturday and
contains three months. The first month has 31 days, the
second 30, and the third 30. This too is repeated in the
other quarters. A pleasing and ordered variety is thus
assured.

For the first time the various units of the calendar—
the days, weeks, months, or seasons all come together in
perfect equation on the last day of every quarter. It does
not matter whether the family budget or business accounts
are figured on the day, week, month, season, or quarter
basis. They all agree four times every year. By thus
giving to all these units their full recognition, perfect
balance is secured. The World Calendar is balanced in
structure, perpetual in form, regular in arrangement, divisible in its entirety, and comparable from year to year.

Holidays, whenever convenient to national groups, will
fall on Monday. Christmas will naturally fall on Monday, leaving its familiar date, December 25, unchanged.

In contrast the alternative plan of thirteen months
is in its very number 13, awkward and inconvenient. Who
would want to figure accounts with the unbalanced and
non-divisible number 13, or who would want a 13-hour
clock? The drastic proposal to shorten every month to
28 days of four weeks, forces the arbitrary invasion, between June and July, of a thirteenth month, which is

called Sol. This necessitates a redisposition of 337 days: only the first 28 days in January of the present calendar remain as they are.

In the next few years the League of Nations will call an international conference to discuss the subject of reforming the calendar, and at that time it is believed definite action will be taken regarding one of the two plans which I have outlined to you today. There is something every one of us can do to promote calendar reform. We can talk, discuss and work for The World Calendar, the 12-month revision, which in arrangement, like the clock, is so simple, so natural and so workable.

XVI

PROGRESS IN AMERICA

*Report to members of World Calendar Association,
October, 1934*

AMERICAN interest in calendar reform has been increasing steadily since the subject first came to
public attention, but particularly during the past
year. Gradually an informed public opinion has grown
up, which is convinced that there are real and preventable
inconveniences caused by the changeability and irregularity of the present calendar.

In government circles in the United States, the movement for calendar reform has been looked upon with a
sympathetic eye, but until recently it was not felt that
the time was ripe for any official action or statement of
policy. Lately, however, there has come such a statement of policy from the report of a presidential committee,* which says that "the influence of the federal
government and of other public bodies should be thrown
wherever possible behind investigations, and behind educational movements, which may ultimately lead to its correction." It recommended that governmental and unofficial
agencies call attention to the effects of calendar irregularities, which may lead to calendar simplification.

Studies of the actual questions involved in calendar

* President Herbert Hoover's Research Committee on Social
Trends, January, 1933.

reform, and of the possible effects of calendar revision on various sections of American life, are being carried on in the U. S. Department of Commerce, the U. S. Bureau of Standards, the U. S. Naval Observatory, and other departments and bureaus. The American example of investigation and fact-finding may be shortly followed by England, France, Germany and other governments.

Meanwhile, the U. S. Department of State has undertaken to clear the way for unimpeded American participation in international action on the calendar question, whenever other leading nations are ready. It is worth while recording the steps which have been taken by the American government toward international action: First, the government in 1928 officially indicated to the other nations its willingness to participate in international conferences on calendar reform; second, it has joined 25 other nations in approving an international pact urging the stabilization of Easter by ecclesiastical authorities; third, the American diplomatic delegate has approved at Geneva an international pronouncement as to the desirability in principle of securing a simpler measure of time, more accurately appropriate to the needs of modern economic and social life, and also advocating further international conferences based on the agreed premise that simplification of the calendar is a definite question capable of discussion between nations in the course of official deliberations.

American informed opinion is agreed that the changing features of the present calendar which require attention from the viewpoint of any proposed reform are as follows: (1) The calendar is never the same from year to year; (2) Succeeding years never begin on the same day of the week; (3) Each year it is necessary to use a new calendar; (4) Holidays constantly shift from year to year; (5) Dates of the month fall on different weekdays in successive years; (6) Months in successive years have not the same number of the various weekdays nor the same arrangement of weeks.

Any reform which seeks to meet these problems of changeability must aim, *with the minimum of disturbance of the existing system,* to stabilize and give permanency to the calendar, so as to obtain dependability and comparability from year to year.

In addition to these problems of changeability, there are also certain calendar irregularities which should be remedied in any revision. These irregularities may be stated as follows: (1) The uneven length of the months— 28, 29, 30 and 31 days; (2) There is one month of 28 or 29 days; four months of 30 days; seven months of 31 days; (3) This uneven distribution of days to the months results in varying quarters—90, 91 and 92 days, causing discrepancies of more than 2 per cent in quarterly comparisons and calculations; (4) The half-year divisions are also unequal—the first half has 181 or 182 days, the second half 184 days.

In respect of these irregularities, the purpose of calendar reform, as viewed in America is: to establish an ordered, balanced and equalized arrangement of the time divisions within the yearly calendar.

Government officials have noted that specific examples of calendar errors in existing government statistics may be found in practically every federal department. According to the Bureau of Efficiency in Washington, such calendar errors are present in acute form, for example: in the important tabulations of employment in industrial turnover collected by the Department of Labor; in the statistics of domestic and foreign trade kept by the Department of Commerce; in the records of custom receipts and internal revenue collections, of disbursements by government disbursing officers, recorded by the Treasury Department; in the figures of estimated and actual expenditure and revenue, gathered by the Bureau of the Budget; in the statistics of passports and citizenship kept by the State Department.

Still other official examples of calendar irregularities are pointed out in a study made by the former Governor of New Jersey, who states:

> Some of the inconveniences of the present calendar are obvious to anyone who has had experience in the courts, in legislation or in Government. Because month dates and weekdays fail to synchronize, lawyers and legislators are forced continually to resort to such awkward circumlocutions as "the first Monday after the second Saturday," and "or if said day be a legal holiday then on the next succeeding day not a holiday." The courts are frequently occupied with lawsuits arising out of calendar errors or misunderstandings, usually due to the fact that the anniversary of an event seldom falls on the same day of the week as the event itself. . . . Calendar irregularities crop up in finance, banking, accounting, shipping, insurance, investment, labor, production, real estate and many other activities. Even though we have become accustomed to these inconveniences, they nevertheless exist and exact their price in time and energy.

Business advantages of an improved calendar are summed up in a survey published by the Kiwanis Clubs of America, an organization of business leaders, which points out certain definite savings of time, inconvenience and annoyance together with a greater regularity, availability and accuracy in statistics, accounts and records.

Studies of calendar reform in Washington have included, in many cases, a comparison of the merits of the two major proposals for revision of the Gregorian system. Most of the available reports and opinions are strongly in favor of the 12-month equal-quarter plan as against the 13-month scheme.

The case against the 13-month calendar from the statistical standpoint is presented by Henry W. Bearce, U. S. Bureau of Standards, in a publication officially approved by the Director of the Bureau of Standards of the U. S. Department of Commerce. This document quotes, with full agreement and approval, a summary by Prof. Clark Warburton of the Brookings Institution, pointing out the disastrous effects on historic and business records of a 13-month revision:

> To re-compute the numerous indexes of prices, industrial production and other phases of economic activity would be a costly procedure. In the case of many of the statistical series linking present with past, it would be impossible to convert records of the past into form comparable with the present. . . . The next few years are certain to be critical years in the world's history. Economic changes are extremely rapid. Economic systems are challenging each other. There is great uncertainty. . . . To meet this demand for business stabilization and for national economic planning it is essential that economists and business men have all the aid possible from past records. A radical change in the calendar would seriously reduce the usefulness of these records and hamper adjustment to world needs at a critical time in the advance of civilization.

In the U. S. Navy Department, the subject of calendar reform was formally referred to the Naval Observatory for a study of its merits. The resulting report, combining the viewpoints of naval officers and astronomers, is a

unanimous approval of calendar reform and a recommendation for the adoption of the 12-month equal-quarter
plan. From the viewpoint of mariners, the preservation
of the 12-month division of the year is of highest importance, and the U. S. Navy therefore takes its stand as a
staunch opponent of any 13-month proposal.

In the U. S. Bureau of Foreign and Domestic Commerce, Mr. Walter Mitchell, Jr., has undertaken a study
of certain calendar reform problems, from the particular
viewpoint of their bearing on trade accounting.
Mr. Mitchell in a report recently published shows that
definite confusions, inefficiencies and increased expenditures arise in any system of 13-period accounting.

From the educational standpoint, Dr. W. T. Bawden,
former Assistant Commissioner of the U. S. Office of
Education, has prepared a report showing the importance
of calendar reform to schools and colleges. "Simplification of the calendar is greatly needed in the educational
field," he declares. "It is hoped that the movement will
eventuate in some form of perpetual calendar; that is, one
that does not vary from year to year. The 13-month
calendar has much to commend it, but it would seem that
the objections against the division of the year into 13 units
are sufficiently weighty to prevent its adoption. The
unique advantage of the year of 12 months is that the
divisibility of this number facilitates the keeping of records
and the making of comparisons by periods of varying
length. It will be greatly to the advantage of educators
if some practicable plan for simplifying the calendar can
be carried into effect."

In a recent compilation of opinions from government
officials, made by the United Press, the replies showed 80
per cent favoring the 12-month proposal. Among em-

ployees of the Department of Agriculture, the proportion was even larger, indicating that agricultural interests will inevitably prefer the more moderate reform.

O. E. Baker, of the U. S. Bureau of Agricultural Economics, has stated that the 12-month equal-quarter plan would result in material economy and greater accuracy in statistical information. Leroy E. Peabody, Senior Highway Economist for the U. S. Bureau of Public Roads, favors the many clear-cut advantages of the 12-month revision. James Spear Taylor of the U. S. Department of Commerce has declared that the 12-month plan would have substantial public benefits and great savings.

In addition to the work which government agencies are doing to promote calendar reform, there is a growing activity among civil and business groups of various kinds. Business studies have been made, or are being made, by such varied organizations as the New York State Chamber of Commerce, the American Statistical Association, the National Electric Light Association, the National Fraternal Congress, the American Association of Engineers, and others.

The churches, too, are keenly interested, and their interest is by no means confined to the reform of the church calendar. Church leaders of all Protestant denominations, under the leadership of the Federal Council of Churches and the Universal Christian Council, have ruled by an almost unanimous vote that "general calendar reform is of such social importance that the churches should definitely participate." A poll of leading American clergymen, undertaken for the information of the Universal Christian Council, showed them favoring calendar reform by a vote of 9 to 1, and preferring the 12-month equal-quarter plan, as compared with the 13-month plan, by about 7 to 1. Among American churches, definite official action for calendar reform has recently been taken by the General Convention of the Protestant Episcopal Church, the Biennial Convention of the United Lutheran Church, the General Council of the Presbyterian Church and the College of Bishops of the Methodist Episcopal Church South. Most of the other important Protestant church bodies are preparing to take similar steps at their approaching conventions, the only reason for their delay being that these bodies generally meet only at intervals of two, three or four years.

Meanwhile, in the Roman Catholic church, leadership for calendar reform has been undertaken by Dr. Edward S. Schwegler, a prolific writer for the church press, who has gathered a stalwart body of clergy and laity as supporters of the 12-month plan. Catholic interest in the American movement for calendar reform is indicated by the fact that the membership of The World Calendar Association includes 18 Roman Catholic archbishops and bishops and about 200 priests.

In view of the steady progress of the movement for calendar reform in the United States during the past year, the studies and investigations into the subject have largely centered on a comparison of the two major proposals for a perpetual calendar, the 12-month and 13-month plans.

In some cases, the issue has been slightly confused by the unwarranted emphasis laid by advocates of the 13-month plan on the fact that a certain number of American businesses have adopted a 4-week period for their internal accounting. Such an accounting system is, of course, in no way identical with, or equivalent to, a 13-month calendar, and accountancy experts point out that many various divisions of the year are employed by different types of business and scientific activity for convenience in calculations and records. Astronomers, for example, ignore the calendar in many of their records, using instead the precise numbered day from an arbitrarily fixed date 6647 years ago, so that January 1, 1934, is designated by them as "2427439, Julian Day." Churchmen use an ecclesiastical calendar which differs in many ways from the civil calendar, but which is satisfactory for their "internal accounting." Governments and business firms use a "fiscal year" which frequently begins at a different period than the civil calendar. Accountants group the year, for bookkeeping purposes, in many various ways according to the nature of the business concerned. But all this would seem to have no real connection with the proposed revision of the civil calendar, and the effort of 13-month calendar advocates to apply a 13-period accounting system to all of man's activities, whether social, professional, scientific, economic, religious, or educational, would seem to be not only an absurdity, but an injustice as well.

In the consideration of calendar reform, the choice lies between a moderate revision, sane and constructive, and an extreme reform with an inevitable heritage of upheaval and difficulty. Past history has shown the impossibility of imposing an extreme reform of the calendar. The French Revolution sought to install a completely new calendar with a 10-day week and various other novel innovations; the result was a chaos and confusion that compelled restoration of the Gregorian system within a few years. More recently, in Russia, an attempt was made to install a new calendar, with a rotating 5-day week and other radical departures from the Gregorian system.

It was an interesting experiment, but proved so unworkable that it has been gradually modified.

Informed public opinion in America, as in Europe, votes overwhelmingly for moderation and reasonableness in calendar reform. Repeated questionnaires of various cross-sections of American opinion indicate this very clearly. For instance, a questionnaire addressed by the United Press to members of the American Statistical Association, including representatives of the most important business and industrial organizations in the country, showed a vote of 294 for the 12-month plan, as compared with 117 for the 13-month proposal. A questionnaire addressed to leading American clergymen by the same press association showed a vote of 907 for the 12-month plan, as compared with 131 for the 13-month proposal. A questionnaire addressed to bankers by the University Association for the Study of Calendar Reform showed a preference for the 12-month plan of 322 to 112. Educators (mostly university professors) were registered by the University Association as 244 to 124 for the 12-month plan, while a smaller poll by the United Press resulted in a verdict of 65 to 26 in favor of a 12-month revision. Transportation officials, polled by the University Association, were 123 to 33 for the 12-month plan; astronomers gave the same verdict by 83 to 33.

Some of these questionnaires involve comparatively small numbers of replies, but the uniformity of the results indicates that they represent a fair average cross-section of informed American opinion. The percentages favoring the 12-month plan, as against the 13-month proposal, in these various polls, are as follows: statisticians 71.5 per cent; clergy 87.3 per cent; bankers 74.2 per cent; educators 66.3 and 71.4 per cent; transportation officials 78.8

per cent; astronomers 71.5 per cent.   (Average, 81.7.)

It may be interesting to compare these percentages with those obtained in England through somewhat similar questionnaires issued by the British Parliamentary Committee on Calendar Reform.   Preference for the 12-month revision of the calendar, as shown by mayors of British towns and cities, was 74.6 per cent; by labor officials 85.3 per cent; by Members of Parliament 65.9 per cent; by a general list of representative Englishmen, members of the League of Nations Union of Great Britain, 90.8 per cent.

The arguments which are cited as chiefly influencing the American preference for the 12-month plan and opposition to the 13-month are:

1. The perpetual 12-month plan accomplishes all the necessary improvements without violence or upheaval. The changes suggested are few and easy of adoption. They can be put into effect almost without being perceived, without inconvenience to anyone, and without seriously disturbing traditional dates, anniversaries and chronological traditions.

2. The 12-month year is divisible by months into halves, quarters, thirds, sixths and twelfths. In arrangement it is harmonious, ordered and balanced. On the other hand, 13 is a prime number, completely indivisible, and a 13-month revision would destroy the convenient quarterly and half-yearly division, which have always been the basic and natural units for a vast volume of records, statistics and accounting.

3. The 13-month plan involves a $\frac{1}{12}$ increase in costs of bookkeeping, billing, collections and other monthly operations. From a practical viewpoint it would mean doing 13 times annually what hitherto has been done 12 times a year. All the monthly activities of the home, business or profession, such as attending meetings, paying bills, servicing machinery and making tabulations, would have to be repeated once more every year.

4. Twelve is an exceptionally convenient number for calculations, and calendar calculations are more often used by the average individual than any other measurements. Under a 13-month calendar all monthly figuring of budgets, time, production, interest and payments of various kinds, would have to be figured in terms of a thirteenth of a year. The number 13, which is difficult to figure with, would occur billions of times a year in everyday reckoning. The extraordinary convenience of the number 12 would give way to the unparalleled inconvenience of the number 13.

5. The transitional period involved in the adoption of a 13-month year would be an era of confusion, and the disarrangement of statistics and historical records would be enormous. Comparisons of present and past would become a matter of guess-work owing to the displacement of the compared periods caused by introduction of a 13th month and by dislocation of seasonal divisions in the general upheaval. The 13-month calendar would vitiate many of the existing statistical records for purposes of comparison, greatly reducing the extent to which the world can guide itself by past experience.

6. Costs of the transitional period would be enormously larger for the 13-month revision than for the 12-month plan. It would also involve greater confusion, legal controversy and other disturbance to trade and industry.

7. A 13-month calendar could not possibly be inaugurated universally. The conception of a year as having 12 months is so deeply ingrained in the minds of the masses that a 13-month year would be understood by only a small proportion of the world's population.

8. International acceptance of a 13-month calendar is impossible. Italy, Sweden, Holland, Belgium, Switzerland, Greece and Chile have definitely stated that they will not consider such a plan, although none of them see any difficulties to a 12-month revision. Japan opposes a 13-month year as contrary to the religion, custom and basic cultural background of the Orient. And there is not the slightest prospect of Great Britain, France, Germany and

Spain accepting any change so revolutionary in character and so opposed to their traditional instincts.

9. The 12-month revision attains a highly desirable symmetry which is not present in the 13-month plan. Every quarter is identical. In every quarter the various calendar units synchronize. No matter what periods of time are used for accounting, recording or calculating—whether it be the day, week, month, season or quarter—they all come together four times a year. This synchronization facilitates the assembling, studying and comparing of reports, records and data of all kinds, whether in business, education, the church or social and family life. The quarterly division gives a clearer perspective and wider outlook than is possible with the smaller units of month, week or day.

10. The 13-month plan would provoke popular prejudice by its use of the number 13 and by the fact that the 13th day of every month would fall on Friday.

11. The farmer, who is still a dominant group in many nations and a very powerful group in all, will not tolerate a 13-month calendar. With its discarding of the quarterly seasons and its complete unheaval of monthly dates, it would create chaos in the reckonings of agriculture. All the traditions, statistics, records and lore of the farmer are bound up with the calendar, and his livelihood is dependent on his knowledge of dates and seasons. He will not accept any new calendar which departs too radically from the systen of time reckoning now in use.

12. Inadequate as the existing calendar is, it is preferable to a 13-month system. The latter would not simplify; it would render the calendar more complex. It would be a backward type of reform, and the economic cost of the new system would be greater than the gain to be realized. Any calendar reform which adds or suppresses months, or which proposes to change the method of seasonally dividing the year, offers more inconveniences than advantages, and it also has the insuperable obstacle of imposing on the human race a complete breakdown of universal habits which are most difficult to change.

In the United States, and indeed throughout the world, there is a growing and insistent conviction that the time has come for another attempt to reform the calendar. Events of the past few years have effectively weakened the tendency of the past to dominate the present, and there is a universal desire for improvements in the economic and cultural structure wherever these are needed. The idea of change meets less resistance from those who normally oppose any departure from long established practice.

The present calendar has been brought under the searchlight of reasonable examination and has been found wanting. A growing knowledge of the proposals made by advocates of the 12-month equal-quarter plan has convinced an increasing group of leaders that in international practice it is the ideal form of revision. People who have been filled with dismay at the suggestion of a 13-month calendar have taken new heart again when they have studied this more moderate and rational proposal, and it has become evident that it was not opposition to reform of any kind which alarmed and distressed them, but fear of changes as extreme and devastating as those proposed by advocates of a 13-month calendar.

American supporters of calendar reform prefer The World Calendar because it is simple, practical and moderate. In its symmetrical arrangement, all the subdivisions of the year unite in a convenient and harmonious equality and unity. No one division or unit of the year dominates over the others in this plan. To it one might well apply the familiar motto of the American republic, *E pluribus unum*—out of many, one. As the states of the republic are united to form a harmonious nation, so each unit of the calendar, while performing its own part, combines with the others to form a united and balanced whole.

Among national legislators who have urged calendar reform, Senator A. Harry Moore, of New Jersey, has definitely advocated American leadership in the movement. In giving his views on this subject in a magazine article published in 1932, before he was a member of the U. S. Senate, he said:

> Calendar reform is not a political question. If any attempt is made to put it into party politics, the attempt should be scotched. For it is a question wholly of scientific, industrial and human efficiency and comfort, which becomes an absurdity if treated on a basis of partisan advantage. It is a question of a fundamental and desirable simplification in everyday life. Sane and practical revision of the calendar is undoubtedly desirable. Standardization in the use of time has become important, and if the calendar can be placed on a sounder economic basis, this will make for savings in convenience, expense and friction which should be reflected in better and less wasteful management, alike in the home, in business and in government.
>
> Revision is an international question, with which no nation can deal single-handedly and alone. Before anything definite can actually be put into effect, there must be a meeting of the minds of many different peoples and governments. The initiative, however, may very properly come from the United States, as it did 50 years ago in the world-wide adoption of Standard Time. I see no reason why our national government should not inaugurate a study of the question, so that the whole discussion of it in the United States will be on a formal and official basis.

The international aspects of calendar reform become highly important as the subject approaches the stage of actual legislation. Only by mutual agreement among many nations can a change be put into effect. No single nation can act alone in this matter. It is expected that the League of Nations will take definite action in 1936 to set in motion the machinery of international legislation. As there is no political or nationalistic bias to calendar revision, all parties and nations can unite amicably in its accomplishment. In fact, advocates of this reform point out that the movement exercises a world-wide influence in the direction of international cooperation and world peace.

XVII

CHURCH COOPERATION

Lansford, Pennsylvania, June 11, 1935

WE are assembled here to discuss the subject of calendar reform. It is entirely fitting that the clergy and the church should take an active part in this subject. For the reforms through which our calendar has moved in the past were achieved mainly by priests, whether in their churchly roles or as astronomers and rulers.

The foundation of our present calendar was laid down by the priestly scientists of Egypt, to which in great part the knowledge from Babylonia and Chaldea contributed. Leaders of the ancient Jews established for us the weekdays with the one day of rest. The famous Julian calendar, offspring of the Egyptian and predecessor of the Gregorian, was fashioned by Julius Caesar, who as Pontifex Maximus was the religious head of ancient Rome. The Julian calendar, as we all know, was reformed by Pope Gregory in 1582.

Thus it is natural that the churches today should take a part in any further reform that seems necessary. Certainly every churchman should be informed on the subject, first as to why calendar reform is necessary, and second, as to how it will affect the church calendar—how Easter with its corresponding religious holidays will be fixed or stabilized and how the work of the churches will be benefited.

Irregularities and inequalities of the calendar can be corrected very simply, if only we can get international agreement and action. It is very evident that the old calendar no longer suffices. We demand one that is consistent with our new era, one that is simple, accurate and perpetual, one that we can learn as easily and readily as our alphabet or multiplication table. Calendar reform is an essential need. It is a constructive and progressive change, necessary for our development and for our future welfare.

There is another important and significant feature in connection with calendar reform. With the world ever growing smaller through modern transportation and communication, a uniform standard calendar for world usage becomes imperative. As the old sailing vessel of Columbus' day is replaced by the gigantic self-propelled *Normandie,* as the old-fashioned horse-and-buggy is now the modern automobile, as man's swiftest method of travel is now supplemented by the winged airplane of the sky, as the slow method of communicating by handwriting or by word of mouth is now augmented by the rapidly moving keys of the typewriter, by the telephone, telegraph and radio,—so our age-old calendar must be revised if it is to keep in step with progress.

In olden days, revision of the calendar was a matter which could be achieved by edict or by the autocratic decision of one man. Today it must be done in a far more comprehensive way. It is no longer solely for the churches and scientists to solve. Many governments, peoples, educational and business groups must be consulted. They are all directly concerned and actively taking part in the movement for a new calendar. In its very nature, the reform goes beyond national, religious, political and geographical boundaries. It brings together all these different factors and in truth forms one of the strongest unifying bonds that we have today.

At the same time, it must not be allowed to become the exclusive possession of any selfish interest, all activities must be recognized. For example:—Bankers would like the year arranged with precise divisions for interest payments; railroad and shipping executives look at it from the viewpoint of time-tables and train schedules; hotel people regard it from the statistics of their business, which show that certain weekdays are more lucrative than others; merchants want to see whether the new calendar will regulate their affairs on a more profitable basis; statisticians and accountants demand a perpetual calendar which will make their figures and statements more comparable from year to year; agriculture desires greater accuracy and regularity within the equalized quarterly-divisions of the year which correspond to the familiar seasons.

Schools and colleges seek to have vacation days stabilized so that important events can be arranged to occur at certain stated times. In the social world, too, a better coordination between the days of the months and the weekdays would be a great help in the planning of invitations and engagements; and in the field of amusements, an ordered and perpetual calendar would facilitate the arrangement of dates for lectures, exhibitions, concerts and opening nights for the theatre and opera, which frequently call for planning a year in advance.

The groups mentioned are an indication of how important and far-reaching calendar reform will be in its effect. It belongs to and includes every activity,—industry, accounting and economics, religion, science, agriculture, administration, social life and education. The reform thus must harmonize, as far as possible, all the requirements in our very diversified life. Such a reform, providing an ordered, equalized, stable and balanced calendar, perfectly adapted to our modern needs, will bring benefits to every man and woman and child in every walk of life.

We now come naturally to the question that is of particular interest to us, who are gathered here today. Where would Easter be fixed in a new calendar, and what effect would its stabilization have on other religious feast days?

This year (1935) we all observed how confusing is our shifting Easter which, between last year and this year, varied by three weeks, or 21 days. Similarly all the other attendant holidays, such as Ash Wednesday, Palm Sunday, Whitsunday and the Trinity Sundays, shifted also. This wandering characteristic of Easter is regarded by many as of the greatest disadvantage to the church. For upon the early or late Easter depends the length of the church year. It is customary, I believe, to begin certain church activities with the first Sunday in Advent and to conclude with Easter Sunday, or in other words, the period of Christ's life from Advent to the Resurrection. In my own church, the active and social life of the congregation falls within this period, while the Trinity Sundays are used for vacations and for program planning for the coming winter. To have a short church year with an early Easter, or a long church year with a late Easter, brings obvious difficulties. A definite Sunday for Easter has been advocated by leaders of all the great denominations for many years.

It is pertinent to recall here a historical fact. At the time of the Gregorian reform in 1582, certain Catholic leaders wanted Easter stabilized while the rest of the calendar was under consideration, and Pope Gregory himself favored a fixed Easter. But he was hesitant about making too many changes at once and hoped that the Easter question and the regulating of the calendar would be taken up after the necessary leap-year adjustment, which called for immediate attention, had been accepted.

You may remember that Martin Luther wrote as follows regarding the Gregorian reform: "How much better it would have been to have dropped entirely the Mosaic law referring to Easter, rather than patch it up. They should have laid down a special date for the Passion, death and Resurrection, just as has been done for Christmas, Epiphany, Candlemas and other feasts which are fixed and not movable, so that everybody might know exactly, and without trouble or dispute, the dates of Easter and the feasts depending on Easter."

So the proposals to fix Easter are nothing new. Certainly they are not sacrilegious. They are merely an effort to accomplish a much-belated and much-needed reform.

The origin of our wandering Easter is of course known to all of you. It was linked to the first full moon of spring because the early Christians were still very close to their Jewish origin and custom, and they wished to keep the connection between the Resurrection and the Jewish Passover moon. In addition, the full moon had a practical significance, in that its light was required to guide the pilgrims and protect them from the dangers of the road. As for its sentimental significance, let me quote from an eminent English authority: "The full moon shone on Gethsemane on the night of the betrayal, bathing the garden in brilliant light against which the shadows showed deep and black. By the light of the same moon, shining through their casements, the women had prepared the spices and embalments. By the light of the setting moon, they met and went before it, on the first Easter daybreak, to the Sepulchre. When they turned their footsteps home, the *Moon* of Judaism had set and the *Sun* of Christianity had arisen."

There is one very important argument for Easter stabilization which is often overlooked. When coupled with calendar reform, it would forever remove the difference in the days of observance now prevailing in the Near East, where the Gregorian and Julian calendars conflict. This lack of coordination hinders united worship and keeps alive the estrangement between various church groups. In Yugoslavia, for instance, Roman Catholics and Greek Catholics observe Easter on different Sundays. A new calendar, if accepted by both sides, would make for cooperation and friendship.

In the opinion of many church leaders, the demand to fix Easter and its corresponding festivals is assuming far-reaching and significant importance because a universal celebration of Easter throughout Christendom would promote unity among the churches and encourage a spiritual bond between Christians everywhere. This greater unity would be a potent and vital force that could not be denied or ignored.

Easter, in The World Calendar, will come always on April 8, the 99th day of the year, and the historical anniversary of the Resurrection. With Easter always coming on the same day, all the other dependent feast days fall in beautiful order. Ash Wednesday comes on February 22; Palm Sunday on April 1; Good Friday April

6; Whitsunday May 26; Trinity Sunday June 3. With this new order and symmetry, six months from Advent Sunday, December 3, to Whitsunday, May 26, might well be devoted to the Life of Christ in the church year, and six months from Trinity Sunday, June 3, to December 3, might be devoted to the Trinity Sundays. There would always be exactly 25 Sundays after Trinity.

The great Eastern Orthodox Church, through the official representative of the Oecumenical Patriarch at Constantinople, has made an official declaration endorsing a fixed Easter and supporting the 12-month equal-quarter reform. The Universal Christian Council adopted a resolution last August approving the stabilization of Easter and advocating calendar reform. In America, the Federal Council of Churches is sympathetic to both movements.

The Episcopal Church at its General Convention in Atlantic City, passed a resolution urging Easter stabilization and calendar revision. Similar resolutions were passed by the General Council of the Presbyterian Church, the United Lutheran Church, and the College of Bishops of the Methodist Episcopal Church South.

Meanwhile, the Roman Catholic Church has made no formal declaration of approval, but the Pope, through his representative, the Papal Nuncio at Berne, Switzerland, has stated to the League of Nations that no dogmatic difficulties exist. The movement for calendar reform inside the Catholic Church has grown rapidly. Eighteen bishops and archbishops are members of The World Calendar Association, together with several hundred priests, scattered throughout the world. Latin America, which is Catholic, has declared itself through church and state as favoring reform, and some of the foremost leaders of the

Church in Chile, Argentina, Mexico and other countries are heading the movement.

How and when will it all come to the practical stage of enactment? The general reform of the calendar will come up at the League of Nations shortly, in a meeting which should lead ultimately to the drafting of a treaty to be presented to all nations for ratification before 1939.

As for the actual putting into effect of a stabilized Easter, you as churchmen know better than I, how this may ultimately be brought about. Certainly a definite pronouncement from the Vatican would help. The other churches have mostly expressed themselves as far as they can, until some gesture from Rome makes unity on this subject possible. Such a statement from the Vatican may be expected, I believe, within the next year or two.

Meanwhile we in America should do our utmost to prepare our own denominations for the greatest step in religious cooperation which the world has ever seen. We should study, work and talk toward it. We should see that our denominational bodies pass the strongest possible resolutions for it.

Calendar reform is a matter of human interest and welfare. It is a cause that merits wholehearted cooperation, not merely of the civil world, but also of religion, the churches and the clergy. It is one of the few world projects upon which it is possible to obtain international agreement among nations without fear of offending some prejudices, some special interest, or some national bias.

XVIII

LORD DESBOROUGH'S LEADERSHIP

Report to members of World Calendar Association,
April, 1936

ON March 4, 1936, the British government formally announced its position on calendar reform. The announcement was made quietly with the restraint of official language, from the floor of the House of Lords. It stated that the British delegates at Geneva would give "most sympathetic" consideration to the question of calendar revision which is scheduled for submission to a League of Nations commission this fall.

The government commitment was so worded that its full significance was lost to many of the listeners, as it may even be lost at first reading to many of those who only give a cursory glance at the official text.

But its significance was not lost to Lord Desborough, the persevering leader whose steady devotion to the cause of calendar reform has at last won for him the prospect of victory which he so richly deserves. He correctly viewed the announcement as his government's official declaration of policy in favor of a revised calendar.

Lord Desborough's interest in calendar reform dates back prior to the World War, when he became interested in the beginnings of the movement on the Continent. He followed its early development in Switzerland and Germany. Then, after the war, he saw it reappear, and he sought to enlist British support in Parliament as early as 1920 and 1921. Finding that British interest was more stirred by the possibility of a fixed Easter than by the more comprehensive suggestion of general calendar revision, he decided to campaign, for the time being, on Easter stabilization as a first stage in the larger reform. He slowly won the hesitating support of British leaders in church and state. At parliamentary hearings in 1920 and 1921, he saw the Archbishop of Canterbury give a qualified approval of his plans regarding Easter. Eventually in 1928, after nearly a decade of adroit and energetic campaigning, he brought the Easter project triumphantly to the floor of Parliament and obtained for it the full approval of both legislative houses. Great Britain's Easter Act was, in fact, the first actual legislation by any country on the subject of reforming the Gregorian calendar.

Eight years passed, however, before Great Britain was ready for the next step, which resulted in the commitment given by Lord Feversham, as government spokesman, in the recent House of Lords debate.

The progress which was made with the British people during the intervening years is indicated by the complete support given to Lord Desborough on this later occasion by the Archbishop of Canterbury. No qualifications accompanied the Primate's official utterance, which, aside from its hearty endorsement of his colleague's viewpoint, was mainly a considered and thoughtful appeal to the other great churches of Christendom to join in the enactment of a new calendar before 1939.

Lord Desborough, at 81, is a British peer who has many ties of friendship and understanding throughout the world. His pre-eminence as a sportsman and as a business leader, aside from his family connection with the Morgan-Grenfell banking house, have helped to make him known in America. As a young man, he climbed the Rockies, swam twice across the Niagara River, and endeared himself to Americans by his prowess and daring. Turning to business, he proved himself the kind of an "organizer" that Americans understand and admire. For the greater part of his business life he was easily the outstanding personage in the Chamber of Commerce movement in England and a familiar figure at international business conventions. Active in politics, he entered public service as William Henry Grenfell, member of the House of Commons, rising later to a peerage and engaging actively in duties on many government committees and public bodies.

Fortunately for the cause of calendar reform, Lord Desborough has never thought of "retiring," even after four-score years. For more than twenty years, he has zealously watched and studied the currents of thought and action that are leading the world today toward an improved calendar. He early realized that the process was a gradual one, that there were obstacles of tradition and usage to be patiently met, without violence or irritation, and that the situation called for persistent and prolonged educational efforts.

He watched the movement for a new calendar grow up in the Eastern Orthodox Church, and was encouraged by the leadership of Prof. Eginitis of Greece, who came to be the official representative of the Ecumenical Patriarchate at all important conventions and conferences dealing with this subject. No less hopefully did he observe the growing sentiment in the Roman church for an improvement in the Gregorian system which was foreseen and hoped for by Pope Gregory 354 years ago.

The part that the churches must necessarily play in any effective international agreement on the calendar was clear to him. He did not unduly urge his own church to action, for he knew that a "level" front was more important than the spectacular advance of an individual unit.

Meanwhile he pursued his activities on the civil side— in governmental, commercial and scientific bodies. There were other earnest leaders, too; and Lord Desborough was the last man to claim sole prerogative of leadership when there were others who were competent, able and willing to guide and direct the movement.

In the early 1920s, the various international activities for calendar reform focussed themselves on the League of Nations. The currents which converged at Geneva included the Swiss government, long an active proponent of calendar reform, the International Astronomical Union, which had early taken the scientific leadership of the cause, and the International Chamber of Commerce, representing business and commercial relationships. Out of these (in none of which Lord Desborough had been entirely absent) grew the organization of a special League committee of inquiry in 1923. On this committee were representatives of the three leading religious groups, seeking to clear the ground completely of dogmatic difficulties. Rome, Constantinople and the Protestant group (represented by the Anglican delegate) agreed in a definite and binding commitment that "no dogmatic obstacle stood in the way of calendar revision." This may have seemed a negative progress to many over-ardent advocates of reform but to Lord Desborough it was signal progress.

By 1931, the nations were ready for their first formal

international convention on the subject. Delegates of 44 nations participated in the lengthy deliberations, which again resulted in a kind of progress which seemed negative to many, but which a more discerning eye could see was another necessary step in clearing the ground for definite action.

That this action will come in October of this year is the hope and belief which was confidently expressed in the House of Lords debate by both Lord Desborough and his strong supporter, the Primate of the Anglican Church. Whether at the postponed quadrennial session of the Commission on Communications and Transit, or at a special meeting called for this express purpose, there can be little reason to doubt that calendar reform will come up for international consideration. And the formal statement of the British government, made through Lord Feversham in answer to the motion of Lord Merthyr, assures the world that Great Britain will stand four-square in a "most sympathetic" and serious support of the new calendar which is advocated by Lord Desborough and a host of far-sighted men and women the world over.

Lord Desborough supplemented his address in a letter published prominently in the London *Times* on March 14, in which he says:

"To the Editor of the *Times:*

"Sir,—In the debate on the Calendar in the House of Lords on March 4, I rejoiced to hear so powerful a voice as that of the Archbishop of Canterbury lifted in support of the plea that the Government should give a definite recommendation to the League of Nations Committee which is to reconsider the question of calendar reform this autumn.

"The case for reform has long been prejudiced by the fact that, of the two schemes selected by the League Committee for final consideration, the plan for dividing the year into 13 months (including a new month called 'Sol' to be inserted between June and July) has till lately received the greater publicity. Most people, however, will agree with Lord Feversham, who, in replying for the Government, quoted from the report of the unofficial Committee on Calendar Reform (1931) the conclusion that a 13-month calendar was 'definitely repugnant to British feeling.'

"The alternative scheme, which, by a slight rearrangement of the days of our present calendar and by treating one day in the year as a day apart, would establish a perpetual year of four equal quarters, is favored by a substantial body of responsible opinion not only in this country and the United States but in many other Christian countries throughout the world.

"It would appear that the active opposition to reform which was mentioned in the reply of the Government was really opposition to the 13-month scheme, and that the allegations of public apathy on the question, although true of 1931, when the Burnham Committee of Inquiry reported, are much less true today. Such a subject as this cannot, of course, be expected to excite the passionate interest of the general public, but it is a fact that many responsible bodies, beginning with the International Chamber of Commerce, which has repeatedly pressed for action, and including in this country many leading chambers of commerce, the National Chamber of Trade, and the Trades Union Congress, have passed resolutions in favour of a moderate scheme of reform. It is within my knowledge that many of these resolutions have been forwarded to the Home Office, though they appear not to have been brought to the notice of Lord Feversham before the debate.

"It is satisfactory that the Government has promised that the question will have the most sympathetic and serious consideration of their representatives at Geneva when the relevant committee considers the matter this autumn. The universal desire in this country for a stabilized Easter has been expressed by the passing through both Houses of the Easter Act of 1928, but pending the general assent of all the Christian communions, which is plainly an essential preliminary, that Act has never been put into operation by the Order in Council required. The movement for a general reform of the calendar has recently developed so widely that the two aspects of reform have now become inseparable. In a fixed calendar, of course, the date of Easter would be stabilized not only on a particular Sunday but also on a particular date in the year.

"Clearly the Government's attitude must be determined in the main by the weight of public opinion behind the movement for reform, and I may perhaps be allowed to express the hope that interested organizations will take the opportunity to acquaint themselves with the questions at issue. These are not by any means so complicated as they have been made to appear, but it is obviously not possible to expound the case for reform and to present the scheme for a fixed calendar within the limits of a letter. There has been published a small booklet explaining the very simple measures proposed, and I should be happy to see that a copy is sent to anyone who applies to me for it.

I am, &c.,
DESBOROUGH.
Taplow Court, Taplow, Bucks."

XIX

U. S. OFFICIAL STATEMENT

*Report to members of The World Calendar Association,
October, 1936. Approved by the Executive Secretary
of the U. S. Central Statistical Board*

FROM Washington comes a government statement on calendar reform, strongly urging revision of the calendar and advocating an international conference to discuss the matter with a view toward obtaining definite enactment of the proposed change.

The statement comes from the Central Statistical Board, a coordinating group of officials representing all departments of the Government and operating under a Cabinet Committee—composed of the Secretary of the Treasury, the Secretary of Agriculture, the Secretary of Commerce and the Secretary of Labor.

The subject of calendar reform came before this Board through a request from the State Department for guidance in international discussions of calendar reform. The Central Statistical Board was asked to make a study of the questions involved and to submit a report which could be used in formulating the policy of the United States Government.

Studies by the Central Statistical Board have been going on for more than a year, and have now resulted in a definite report to the State Department. The report is entirely favorable to the general idea of calendar reform.

It recommends (1) that the United States send representatives to any meeting called by the League of Nations on the subject; and (2) that the United States support proposals for the calling of an international convention on calendar reform.

The report emphasizes "the increasing advocacy of calendar reform in this country" and the "widespread support for a special international convention to discuss the matter thoroughly." It explains that "the need for the establishment of a perpetual calendar is now agreed upon by a very large number of business interests, and is sympathetically viewed by the agencies of the Federal Government dealing with statistics," and continues, "We would urge participation by this country in such an international convention," whose decision thereafter could be presented to the countries of the world for action and adoption.

The Central Statistical Board recognizes and is keenly appreciative of the studies and activities undertaken by the Commission for Communications and Transit of the League of Nations for calendar reform. At the same time the Board notes that the Commission, being chiefly concerned with transportation and communication matters, is not in a position to carry the reform to the actual stage of commitment, and therefore suggests that the Commission should recommend to the League of Nations the calling of a special international convention.

The complete text of the report of the Central Statistical Board, together with the acknowledgment by the State Department, is published in the following note. It is an important document in the history of the world's progress toward a newer and better calendar.

NOTE: The Central Statistical Committee of the United States Government consists of: Daniel C. Roper, Secretary of Commerce; Frances Perkins, Secretary of Labor, (Chairman of the Central Statistical Committee); Henry Morgenthau, Jr., Secretary of the Treasury; and Henry A. Wallace, Secretary of Agriculture. Its subsidiary, the Central Statistical Board, includes the following: Stuart A. Rice, Chairman; Isador Lubin, Vice Chairman, Commissioner of Labor Statistics, Department of Labor; Oscar E. Kiessling, Chief Economist, Mineral Resources and Economics Division, Bureau of Mines; Mordecai Ezekiel, Economic Adviser to the Secretary of Agriculture; E. G. Draper, Assistant Secretary of Commerce; E. A. Goldenweiser, Director, Division of Research and Statistics, Board of Governors of the Federal Reserve System; George C. Haas, Director of Research and Statistics of the Treasury; E. Dana Durand, Commissioner, Tariff Commission; Corrington Gill, Assistant Administrator in charge of Research, Statistics and Finance of the Works Progress Administration; W. H. S. Stevens, Assistant Chief Economist, Economics Division, Federal Trade Commission; Leonard D. White, Commissioner, Civil Service Commission; Ernest M. Fisher, Director, Division of Economics and Statistics, Federal Housing Administration; and Frederick F. Stephan, Secretary-Treasurer, American Statistical Association.

The resolution on calendar reform of the Central Statistical Board is included in the following letter addressed to the Secretary of State, signed by Stuart A. Rice, Chairman:

"My dear Mr. Secretary: With further regard to our letter of March 8, 1935, on the subject of calendar reform and the answer thereto of March 18, 1935 (file WE:570. B5/45), signed for you by the Under Secretary, I am directed by the Central Statistical Board to inform you that we have had the several questions of calendar reform under further consideration. . . . The Central Statistical Board recently held a special meeting at which there were present representatives of the two chief associations interested in calendar reform, together with a number of representatives of Government departments and agencies and non-Government interests. . . . As a result of the discussion at this special meeting, the matter of calendar reform was given further consideration at the last regular meeting of the Board. I am directed to report to you several actions taken by that meeting. . . . The Central Statistical Board recognizes that the United States can take no action with regard to agenda items for the next meeting of the Commission on Communications and Transit of the League of Nations, which, we understand informally may be called into session this autumn. Nevertheless, we believe that the Department of State should be informed of the increasing advocacy of calendar reform in this country and of the wide-spread support for a special international convention to discuss the matter thoroughly. . . . The need for the establishment of a perpetual calendar is now agreed upon by a very large number of business interests and is sympathetically viewed by the agencies of the Federal Government dealing with statistics. The

Board believes that advocacy by the United States of either of the two chief plans of calendar reform at this time would be premature. It is the Board's further belief that the Commission on Communications and Transit of the League of Nations is not the proper body to decide the relative merits of the two chief plans, but that the Commission might be induced to report to the League a recommendation for the calling of an international convention. We would urge participation by this country in such an international convention called to decide upon one plan, which thereafter could be presented to the countries of the world for further action and possible adoption. . . . In the light of these beliefs, the Board has directed me to transmit to you the following resolution:

"BE IT RESOLVED that, if the subject of calendar reform is included as an agenda item for the next meeting of the Commission on Communications and Transit of the League of Nations, the Central Statistical Board hereby requests the Secretary of State to consider the advisability of sending representatives of the United States to such meeting, and BE IT FURTHER RESOLVED that the said Board requests the Secretary of State to consider the advisability of recommending that any delegate or delegates to such meeting be instructed to support a recommendation from the said Commission to the League of Nations that an international conference be called to discuss the several matters pertaining to calendar reform."

The formal acknowledgment of the State Department, addressed to Dr. Rice as Chairman of the Central Statistical Board, is as follows:

"My dear Mr. Rice: I have received your letter of August 4, 1936, informing me of the studies made by the Central Statistical Board on the subject of calendar reform and conveying to me the text of a resolution on the question recently adopted by the Board. . . . I note that the Board recommends in its resolution that the Government of the United States send representatives to the next meeting of the Commission on Communications and Transit of the League of Nations, if the subject of calendar reform is included in the agenda, and that such representatives be instructed to support the proposition that an international conference be called to discuss the several matters pertaining to calendar reform. . . . You may be assured that should an invitation to participate in a meeting of the Commission on Communications and Transit be received, the views of the Central Statistical Board will receive careful consideration by the Department of State.

"Sincerely yours, William Philips, Acting Secretary."

It will be noted that the American declaration is similar in tenor to the official pronouncement made by the British Government last March in the course of the House of Lords debate led by Lord Merthyr, Lord Desborough and the Archbishop of Canterbury, all advocates of calendar revision.   At that time, the spokesman for the British

Government promised that the subject of calendar reform, whenever it came up for consideration at the League of Nations, would have "the most sympathetic and serious consideration of the representatives of His Majesty's Government."

The British statement was interpreted a few days later by Lord Desborough in *The London Times*. He said in part: "It would appear that the active opposition to reform was really opposition to the 13-month scheme, and that the allegations of public apathy on the question, although true of 1931, are much less true today. Such a subject as this cannot of course be expected to excite the passionate interest of the general public, but it is a fact that many responsible bodies have passed resolutions in favor of a moderate scheme of reform. It is satisfactory that the Government has promised that the question will have the most sympathetic and serious consideration of their representatives at Geneva. The movement for a general reform of the calendar has developed widely."

Thus England and the United States, the two great English-speaking nations, are in accord and ready to participate in the movement for a revision of the calendar through a specially-called international convention.

Other countries are aligning themselves with this movement. Germany's attitude, defined at Geneva in 1931, is further emphasized in recent unofficial declarations by the Ministry of the Interior. It is stated yet again in an article published in the October, 1936, issue of the *Journal of Calendar Reform* from the pen of Dr. Walter Simons, former Foreign Minister, Chief Justice and interim President of Germany. Dr. Simons urges the League of Nations to lose no time in the summoning of an international convention on calendar reform.

France, despite financial and political preoccupations, continues its interest in revision of the calendar, energetically advocated at Geneva by Senator Godart and the other French delegates to the International Labor Conference. Senator Godart has recently stated that he proposes to bring this subject up for consideration before the French Senate and to obtain a definite commitment from the French government, aligning it with England, Germany and the United States for immediate international action toward a convention at which a treaty would be drafted for the enactment of a new calendar. The traditional intellectual leadership of France on the European continent has brought forth, during the past few weeks, the most significant book on calendar reform yet published in Europe, "La Question de Paques et du Calendrier." It is written by the Abbé Chauve-Bertrand of Nevers, whose work carries a British endorsement in the preface by the venerable Catholic liturgical scholar, Abbot Cabrol of England.

Italy, Spain, Holland and Belgium continue their long-standing interest in a new calendar and are ready to participate in the proposed international convention. With them are found also the Scandinavian governments, the Baltic nations and the Near Eastern group, including Greece, Yugoslavia and Turkey.

Switzerland was the first European state to advocate calendar reform, and it has legislated further on the subject than any other country in the world. The report of its 1931 calendar committee, recommending international enactment of a revised calendar, was officially approved before the Swiss Parliament and given a full vote of endorsement. Recently the same Swiss Committee has completed a survey of opinion by leading Swiss legal authorities on the internal legislation which will be necessary in connection with the change from the old to the new calendar.

Latin-American countries are a bloc in approving calendar reform. Leadership of this movement is lodged in the Chilean government. The Chilean delegates at Geneva, reinforced by other South American representatives, are earnestly pressing for League of Nations action. Mexico has considered the subject through a committee appointed by the Foreign Office and has obtained a complete agreement among all government departments in support of a revised calendar. Mexican leaders have recently expressed impatience at diplomatic delays and have suggested that the Mexican government is ready to call an international convention, to sit in Mexico City, if the League of Nations should not be in a position to act promptly.

In the Far East, the Japanese government has reiterated the clear stand which it took at the Geneva Conference of 1931.

The attitude of the churches, which was long a reason for international hesitation in calendar reform, has been greatly clarified during the past few months. At Chamby, Switzerland, in August of this year, the Universal Christian Council, central body of all non-Roman churches, concluded its four-year study of calendar revision and declared itself unhesitatingly and most emphatically for a new calendar. The text of the resolution passed by the Universal Christian Council for Life and Work, Chamby, Switzerland, August 25, 1936, is as follows:

WHEREAS the Universal Christian Council at its Eisenach meeting in 1929 expressed its desire for a careful study of calendar reform and Easter Stabilization; and

WHEREAS the Council in 1932 instituted an intensive study of these subjects by its Research Department; and

WHEREAS these studies and reports from the Churches have shown that a reform of the calendar and the stabilization of Easter would, if carried through, receive the support of the overwhelming majority of the Churches, providing it is based upon the perpetual twelve-month equal-quarter plan proposed by the League of Nations;

THEREFORE, be it resolved that the Universal Christian Council instructs its Standing Committee on Calendar Reform, to notify the Secretary General of the League of Nations concerning the above report and to secure the most effective presentation of this action of the Churches at the forthcoming world conference on Calendar Reform and the stabilization of Easter and finally that this Council asks the Churches to inform their respective Governments of this action and of their views with regard to the desirability of adopting the new calendar.

Members of this great ecclesiastical body include the Eastern Orthodox Church, the Church of England, and all the large Protestant Churches of Europe and America. The viewpoint of the Vatican on this subject, too, is gradually being clarified—first, by the report of the Cabrol mission sent to Rome from England, and more recently, by the Abbé Chauve-Bertrand's book.

A wide development of interest in calendar reform is also noticed in other directions. Labor has spoken again and convincingly at the Geneva Conference of the International Labor Office. Commercial bodies, following the long-standing leadership of the International Chamber of Commerce, have been active and resolutions have recently come to the League of Nations from influential British groups, including the London Chamber of Commerce, the Association of British Chambers and the Congress of British Empire Chambers.

Scientific and learned associations which have manifested the widest public interest in the enactment include leading organizations of this kind, both in the United States and England.

The reasons which are behind this steadily growing international interest in the prompt enactment of a revised calendar were well expressed in the debate in the House of Lords last March and in the committee hearing before the International Labor Conference in June.

"If the calendar is reformed," said Lord Merthyr, "it would be of some advantage, direct or indirect, to every man, woman and child in the civilized world," and the Archbishop of Canterbury added: "I have found it impossible to resist the plea for reform in this matter which comes, I think it may be said, with practical unanimity from the representatives of all the great organizations of trade, industry and commerce."

The unanimous resolution passed by delegates of 47 nations at the Geneva Labor Conference declares: "It is a well-recognized fact that the present calendar is very unsatisfactory from economic, social and religious standpoints, and that recent studies, investigations and reports have shown a marked trend of opinion in favor of its revision."

Friends of the League of Nations have seen with keen appreciation the interest which the League has taken in calendar reform, because they view it as one of the subjects on which the League may well advance and strengthen, without friction or difficulty, the purpose of its Charter: *"To promote international cooperation and to achieve international peace and security."* Calendar reform, they point out, offers a timely and welcome opportunity for nations to come together without the handicap of national prejudice, political bias or special interest. The subject is one which aims at the common good and general welfare of mankind without discrimination or barrier. The reason and argument for calendar reform are based on the broad foundation that the natural orderliness and harmony of the universe dictate a corresponding symmetry and order in the system of our time-measurement, which is founded on the immutable movements of the earth and the sun. Here an application is found for the noteworthy statement of Dr. Robert Millikan, that the universe is "of extraordinary and unexpected orderliness and of the wondrous beauty and harmony that go with order" and that there exists "an inter-relatedness, a unity and a oneness about the whole of nature." Or the similar statement of Calvin Coolidge that "the process of civilization consists of the discovery by men of the laws of the universe and of living in harmony with these laws."

A general agreement is being reached among all nations and authorities, as to the type of calendar revision which is required. It should be one in which the laws of the universe are applicable. The 13-month plan has been discarded and the 12-month, equal-quarter plan, known as The World Calendar, which responds more closely to the above-named attributes—law, order, harmony, balance, inter-relatedness, unity and oneness—is accepted as the approved method of revision.

The United States, in the report of the Central Statistical Board, has wisely drawn attention to the urgency of immediate international action for the calling of a treaty-drafting convention, if the world is to have the benefit of an improved calendar within a reasonable time. There are certain stated intervals at which the transition can be effected in an easy and natural way, when both the old and the new calendar coincide by beginning the year on the same day and date—*Sunday, January 1, 1939.* The same opportunity will not occur again until 1950—eleven years later. If, therefore, action by the League of Nations is not taken within the next few months, it becomes imperative for an individual government to take independent action by calling for the necessary international conference. The proper procedure will then be formulated for the operation of the new calendar in 1939. It is greatly hoped, however, that the League, fully aware of its opportunity, will not permit this chance for international cooperation and agreement to pass by and will do everything in its power to bring the new calendar to fulfillment without further delay.

In the House of Lords, Lord Desborough expressed the ardent wish "that this long-needed reform of the calendar and the stabilization of Easter may be introduced to the great advantage of the world in 1939." And, in the words of the Archbishop of Canterbury: "It would be a real misfortune if this matter were allowed to drift."

COMPARISON OF DATES

Table shows 1933, 1939 or 1950 A.D.

Gregorian Calendar: Changes every year. **The World Calendar:** Every year the same.

Week-days	1ST QUARTER Gregorian Calendar	1ST QUARTER World Calendar	2ND QUARTER Gregorian Calendar	2ND QUARTER World Calendar	3RD QUARTER Gregorian Calendar	3RD QUARTER World Calendar	4TH QUARTER Gregorian Calendar	4TH QUARTER World Calendar
Sunday	Jan. 1	Jan. 1	Apr. 2	Apr. 1	July 2	July 1	Oct. 1	Oct. 1
Monday	2	2	3	2	3	2	2	2
Tuesday	3	3	4	3	4	3	3	3
Wednesday	4	4	5	4	5	4	4	4
Thursday	5	5	6	5	6	5	5	5
Friday	6	6	7	6	7	6	6	6
Saturday	7	7	8	7	8	7	7	7
Sunday	8	8	9	8	9	8	8	8
Monday	9	9	10	9	10	9	9	9
Tuesday	10	10	11	10	11	10	10	10
Wednesday	11	11	12	11	12	11	11	11
Thursday	12	12	13	12	13	12	12	12
Friday	13	13	14	13	14	13	13	13
Saturday	14	14	15	14	15	14	14	14
Sunday	15	15	16	15	16	15	15	15
Monday	16	16	17	16	17	16	16	16
Tuesday	17	17	18	17	18	17	17	17
Wednesday	18	18	19	18	19	18	18	18
Thursday	19	19	20	19	20	19	19	19
Friday	20	20	21	20	21	20	20	20
Saturday	21	21	22	21	22	21	21	21
Sunday	22	22	23	22	23	22	22	22
Monday	23	23	24	23	24	23	23	23
Tuesday	24	24	25	24	25	24	24	24
Wednesday	25	25	26	25	26	25	25	25
Thursday	26	26	27	26	27	26	26	26
Friday	27	27	28	27	28	27	27	27
Saturday	28	28	29	28	29	28	28	28
Sunday	29	29	30	29	30	29	29	29
Monday	30	30	May 1	30	31	30	30	30
Tuesday	31	31	2	31	Aug. 1	31	31	31
Wednesday	Feb. 1	Feb. 1	3	May 1	2	Aug. 1	Nov. 1	Nov. 1
Thursday	2	2	4	2	3	2	2	2
Friday	3	3	5	3	4	3	3	3
Saturday	4	4	6	4	5	4	4	4
Sunday	5	5	7	5	6	5	5	5
Monday	6	6	8	6	7	6	6	6
Tuesday	7	7	9	7	8	7	7	7
Wednesday	8	8	10	8	9	8	8	8
Thursday	9	9	11	9	10	9	9	9
Friday	10	10	12	10	11	10	10	10
Saturday	11	11	13	11	12	11	11	11

Day								
...esday (Tuesday)	14	14	16	14	15	14	15	25
Wednesday	15	15	17	15	16	15	16	15
Thursday	16	16	18	16	17	16	17	16
Friday	17	17	19	17	18	17	18	17
Saturday	18	18	20	18	19	18	19	18
Sunday	19	19	21	19	20	19	20	19
Monday	20	20	22	20	21	20	21	20
Tuesday	21	21	23	21	22	21	22	21
Wednesday	22	22	24	22	23	22	23	22
Thursday	23	23	25	23	24	23	24	23
Friday	24	24	26	24	25	24	25	24
Saturday	25	25	27	25	26	25	26	26
Sunday	26	26	28	26	27	26	27	27
Monday	27	27	29	27	28	27	28	28
Tuesday	28	28	30	28	29	28	29	29
Wednesday	Mar. 1	29	31	29	30	29	30	30
Thursday	2	30	June 1	30	31	30	Dec. 1	Dec. 1
Friday	3	Mar. 1	2	June 1	Sept. 1	Sept. 1	2	2
Saturday	4	2	3	2	2	2	3	3
Sunday	5	3	4	3	3	3	4	4
Monday	6	4	5	4	4	4	5	5
Tuesday	7	5	6	5	5	5	6	6
Wednesday	8	6	7	6	6	6	7	7
Thursday	9	7	8	7	7	7	8	8
Friday	10	8	9	8	8	8	9	9
Saturday	11	9	10	9	9	9	10	10
Sunday	12	10	11	10	10	10	11	11
Monday	13	11	12	11	11	11	12	12
Tuesday	14	12	13	12	12	12	13	13
Wednesday	15	13	14	13	13	13	14	14
Thursday	16	14	15	14	14	14	15	15
Friday	17	15	16	15	15	15	16	16
Saturday	18	16	17	16	16	16	17	17
Sunday	19	17	18	17	17	17	18	18
Monday	20	18	19	18	18	18	19	19
Tuesday	21	19	20	19	19	19	20	20
Wednesday	22	20	21	20	20	20	21	21
Thursday	23	21	22	21	21	21	22	22
Friday	24	22	23	22	22	22	23	23
Saturday	25	23	24	23	23	23	24	24
Sunday	26	24	25	24	24	24	25	25
Monday	27	25	26	25	25	25	26	26
Tuesday	28	26	27	26	26	26	27	27
Wednesday	29	27	28	27	27	27	28	28
Thursday	30	28	29	28	28	28	29	29
Friday	31	29	30	29	29	29	30	30
Saturday extra	Apr. 1	30	July 1	*	30	30	31	Y

YEAR-END DAY, December Y, follows December 30th every year

*LEAP-YEAR DAY, June L, follows June 30th in leap years

Both these days are regarded as "extra Saturdays."